Praise for *The*

"What a very special contribution to .... I found the authors' personal experiences, empathy, practical tips, reflection questions, thought exercises and mission to help others captivating. **As an oncologist, I see this book as transformative for my cancer patients, providing a path to live through, with and beyond their cancer."**

–Dean W. Felsher, MD, PhD, Professor of Medicine-Oncology and Pathology, Associate Chief of Oncology, Stanford Medical Center

"I have worked in cancer supportive care for almost 20 years, and this is exactly what I have been wanting for my patients! Like the most wise and caring tour guides you have ever met, the authors know firsthand what this landscape is like, and have helped hundreds of others traverse this challenging terrain."

–Naomi Hoffer, Program Manager, UCSF Division of Neuro-Oncology

"From the chaos and fear of the early days after diagnosis to the aimless unease that lingered after treatment ended, this was the book I searched for but could not find. Twelve years on, the insights and exercises are incredibly useful. Those who are tired of the victim/warrior tropes that seem to dominate the cancer genre will find refuge in these beautiful pages. Cancer is trauma. Here is a roadmap out of the trauma and into wholeheartedness."

–Leslie Purchase, MD, cancer survivor

"For me, this book was an experience, not just an informational book. Shariann and Keri bring such heart to this journey. Reading it and doing the exercises has brought me healing."

–Maggie Constantino, breast cancer survivor and certified Cancer Journey Coach (CCJC)

THE CALL OF
Cancer

THE CALL OF
Cancer

A Loving Pathway to Wholeness, Healing, and Transformation

SHARIANN TOM
KERI LEHMANN

Published by Blue Penny Publishing
For more information, visit www.bluepennypublishing.com

Edited by Mary Reynolds Thompson
Book design by Constellation Book Services, www.constellationbookservices.com

ISBN (paperback): 979-8-9850777-0-4
ISBN (ebook): 979-8-9850777-1-1

Printed in the United States of America

To all those touched by cancer, especially those courageous enough to learn and grow from the experience.

To all of the current and future Cancer Journey Coaches who are helping their clients stand in their power.

CONTENTS

WELCOME

If you have opened this book, chances are you or someone you love has been diagnosed with cancer. A cancer diagnosis, as we know only too well, brings up plenty of fear and lots of questions. "What's going to happen to me? Am I going to die? What do I do?" Pretty soon followed by, "What did I do wrong? Is it my diet? My lifestyle? Why me? I must have made my bed, now I have to lie in it, face the consequences…" and, if you're like us you also ask, "Where is the instruction manual?"

This book serves as the inner guidance we wish we'd had when cancer first entered our lives. In the following pages, we take your hand and walk beside you, showing you that you are not alone and that others have traveled the path before you. We have traveled the path before you. We've worked with hundreds of patients and survivors over the years. We know what they've gone through. So, we've made a roadmap because, what we noticed is that, while every cancer journey is unique, a certain pathway is often followed. Our hope is that this book will not only guide you, it will help you access both self-compassion to aid with your healing and personal power to meet and navigate whatever comes your way.

There is a gap in the world of cancer care. One we have both witnessed and experienced first-hand. The medical world has been focused on treating your physical body. But what about the rest of you? As pioneers in the Life Coaching profession, and as women who have had intimate experiences with cancer, we made the neglected aspect of care our area of specialty. We have developed techniques, tools and models geared toward the emotional, mental, and spiritual aspects of a cancer journey. What we discovered is that while every cancer experience is unique, it usually follows a certain path. A pathway we refer to as The Cancer Journey Roadmap. At certain points along the way, specific opportunities to heal, grow, and awaken present themselves. We are here to help you take full advantage of those opportunities.

It all starts by embracing an outrageous possibility: Cancer can be what heals you.

It all starts by embracing an outrageous possibility: Cancer can be what heals you. We are calling this statement "outrageous" for a reason. And we realize it probably doesn't make sense to you just yet. What we mean is, we see you as so much more than the flesh, bones, and blood of your physical body. We see cancer as a journey of the soul. We believe it's an opportunity to discover and heal parts of yourself that you may not have known how to care for—or known they even existed before. It is an invitation to step into more of your true power and authenticity as a result. So, please stay with us, as this outrageous statement will make much more sense as you continue reading.

We know this is a pretty radical perspective, certainly not one that's held by everybody. After all, a cancer diagnosis is one of the scariest things any of us can imagine. It sucks. And it's also mysterious. Why us? Why now? What just happened? In an effort to make sense of our cancer, we may reach for blame, believing it is the result of something we or someone else did wrong—that our diet, behavior or lifestyle is at fault. Perhaps we should have gone to the gym more, given up the French fries, or worked less hard.

The point is, cancer is not a punishment, and it can be a wake-up call. And we want to give you the gift of this perspective right off the bat.

We see cancer as a journey of the soul. Cancer is not a punishment.

Through these pages, we invite you into the possibility of our "journey" perspective and mindset by sharing our own very personal cancer journeys and those of our clients. We tell you what we went through, what we learned and how we changed as a result. We want you to be able to embrace your cancer journey as a transformative process, and to show you how much power is available when you do.

We'll start by telling you about our own relationships with cancer and some of what has inspired us to do this work in the world.

Shariann's Story: Five Cancer Journeys

I received my first cancer diagnosis in 1998 when I was an ambitious 38 years old. Prior to that I held a high-powered corporate job and ran a household of two little kids (ages four & seven years old), a dog, and a husband. If you asked me if I was happy, I would have said, "Pretty much." I knew that I wasn't completely fulfilled, secretly something was missing, but for that moment, I had a "good life." Then, I got the diagnosis, and everything changed.

I could no longer lead my team, nor do the work that I did to provide financial stability for my family and earn personal accolades for myself. I couldn't do the entire "mommy" and team leader work because cancer treatment drained my energy level and reduced my physical capacity to cope. I had to lean on others. That may not sound so terrible but to a recovering "I-got-it" person, it was everything. The shockwave that reverberated through my life was seismic.

My journey through four bouts of Hodgkin's Lymphoma and one bout of Gastric Intestinal Stomal Tumor (GIST) was going to change my life in ways that I could not imagine. It was my "Incredible Journey." It shifted my priorities, my beliefs, and my values. It changed everything.

In this book, I share my stories with you through each stage of The Cancer Journey Roadmap, a map that Keri and I created because what I wanted most of all was to understand what to expect as I ventured ahead. I wanted to chart my course and manage this new challenge. Truthfully, controlling the path is not possible, but preparing my willingness is. I cannot express how inconceivable and amazing these journeys have been. They led me to my life's work and to creating a movement that would change the way individuals travel their own cancer journeys. And, along the way, it helped me find my true self, my secret missing piece.

Keri's Story: from Caregiver to Patient

My own diagnosis came out of the blue in 2019, a rare form of breast cancer. Truth be told, I thought I knew what I would face after doing this work with clients for seven years. That, on top of having taken caregiver cancer journeys with two significant loved ones and a beloved friend. Well, I soon discovered, it was nothing like the physical, emotional, heart-stopping, heart-opening roller coaster of my own cancer journey as a patient. Strange though it may sound, I went straight to, "What did I do wrong??!" After all, hadn't I been teaching, coaching, and writing against self-blame for the past seven years? Hadn't I already gone through cancer journeys with my husband and my mom? Wasn't I the one who had coached Shariann through her first recurrence and didn't we both marvel at its powerful effects? Well, it turns out that even the co-creator of Cancer Journey Coaching wasn't spared the profound personal struggles that would ensue.

Once I was able to accept my diagnosis, I became (among other things) curious. Because I was already familiar with the roadmap and the tools, I knew cancer was a call to change. But how would I be changed?

As I write this, I'm still integrating and discovering my changes. But one thing I know is, during treatment I really, truly put myself first—something I'd known the importance of in theory but not in practice. This was full permission, no holds barred. I think it rearranged my cells.

If I'm being completely honest, before my diagnosis, I felt a little "on the outs" when it came to the full cancer experience. I hadn't known first-hand that no matter what the prognosis, a cancer diagnosis has you face your mortality. Now, as odd as it might sound, I'm both grateful and honored to have my own cancer experience to share with you, as both Shariann and I walk you through The Cancer Journey Roadmap and all its trials, tribulations, and treasures.

Our combined cancer experience is both broad and deep. As co-authors we cover the spectrum of patient, survivor, and caregiver. When we came together to do this work in the world, we believe we were responding to a calling—a calling to bring more love and healing to those confronting cancer. Our Cancer Journey Coach training programs, our individual work with clients and this book—are all specifically geared toward the life-changing journey that is cancer.

Our Stand

Because this book addresses cancer as a deeply personal journey of the heart and soul, we don't explore available treatments or suggest diets you should follow. These are personal decisions between you and your oncology team, nutritional experts, or any number of specialists you may encounter or choose to consult with. Our focus is on the internal part, the one that includes your beliefs, attitudes, thoughts, feelings, decisions, and choices, what we call your "inner landscape." Our "come-from" is based on many years of helping people with cancer stand in their power and become more of their true selves. We have listened to our clients and in response have developed not only a map, but also the tools and techniques within that map, that you can use immediately for your comfort and well-being, and ultimately for your growth.

Our Promise:
We will be with you every step of the way.

One of the greatest opportunities of this journey is to reconnect with beautiful, often neglected and extremely powerful parts of yourself. We will not only show you how. We will journey with you every step of the way. We want to let you know you are loved and cared for. That you matter. And if all of this sounds like we're speaking a foreign language right now, trust us, it will make a lot more sense to you as you read on.

Taking a cancer journey is not for sissies. And being awake enough to embrace it (notice we didn't say like it) at every stage takes a lot of courage and humility. The courage we are talking about is the courage to be honest with and accepting of yourself. We are talking about the kind of self-honesty and self-acceptance that sets you free and allows you to become more of who you truly are. So, while this process may feel daunting at first, once you embrace it, it becomes liberating.

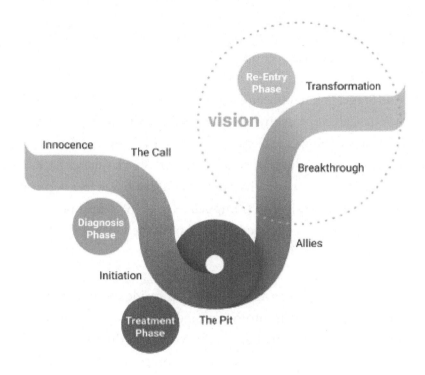

How This Book is Organized

The Cancer Journey Roadmap, which is loosely inspired by mythologist Joseph Campbell's classic arc of The Hero's Journey, takes place in seven stages: Innocence, The Call, Initiation, The Pit, Allies, Breakthrough and Transformation.

Here, in brief, is how the Cancer Journey unfolds:

The Innocence Stage. You begin to suspect or know something is physically wrong. This feeling of dis-ease, which can happen before or after your healthcare professional expresses a concern, puts you on the Cancer Journey Roadmap. It marks a loss of Innocence. At some level you sense life is about to change. What you cannot know is that in the wake of losing one kind of Innocence, you are about to regain another. The dreams and desires that got buried in the rubble of everyday life now have the hope of being uncovered. It is this part of Innocence that offers the first hint of the awakening power of a cancer diagnosis.

The Call Stage. You have been diagnosed with Cancer. This is your new reality. The Call stage, many tell us, feels like being kicked off the edge of a cliff or stepping into a chasm of the unknown. Understandably, this stage includes feelings of shock and fear. Shock that you are called to travel a much different path than you had imagined; fear because the path is still a mystery. Joseph Campbell tells us, "We must be willing to get rid of the life we've planned, so as to have the life that is waiting for us." Well, willing or not, a new life is calling.

The Initiation Stage. Cancer has taken up residence and with it, new terminologies, treatment protocols, and schedules that seem overwhelming. You are literally being initiated into a different way of life. Urgently taking in the information, you prepare to make important decisions and choices about the path your journey will take and the treatments you will choose. You feel anxiety, fear, grief, and uncertainty. But you also learn ways to be in the moment and stay present to yourself.

The Pit Stage. Treatment is now in full swing, and so are its effects. The Pit is characterized by feelings of overwhelm and a swirl of thoughts and feelings that may even include hopelessness. Old ways of pushing through physical and mental limitations are fruitless in the face of the heavy demands of treatment. But challenging as it is, The Pit is also the pivotal part of the cancer journey, where the process of deep and lasting transformation accelerates. This is where you truly begin to heal at a soul level.

The Allies Stage. You emerge from the darkness of The Pit and take your first steps into your new reality. Although quite shaky at first, you become stronger as you begin to surround yourself with Allies who can support you in all aspects of your healing: emotional, spiritual, and physical. Anything or anyone that nurtures and helps you to remember you are more powerful and resourced than you may realize, is an Ally. You realize that support and connection can be found everywhere, with the greatest source being yourself.

The Breakthrough Stage. You begin to see signs that you have changed in big and small ways. You have come to know more of yourself and your needs, and you're beginning to embrace a deeper sense of what is important to you, and to dream of a desired future that may, or may not, look quite different from your pre-cancer life. You recognize that you have been on a journey and have learned a lot about yourself and what makes you happy. Sensing that there is no going back to your pre-cancer self, you begin, energetically, to lean into your future.

The Transformation Stage. You've changed on many levels: body, mind, and spirit. And you feel it at the very core of your being. Now you focus on integrating these changes and embracing the more aware and authentic person you have become. You align with the dreams and visions that give you a greater sense of joy, wisdom, and peace within. The stage of Transformation is positive and life affirming. This is often the stage at which many say, "I wouldn't change my journey for the world."

How to Read this Book

We want you to treat this book as your companion. We've arranged it so you can follow the map to whatever section feels most helpful in the moment and begin there. Or feel free to sink into it in the order it was written. Each chapter includes our stories—Shariann and Keri's, as well as client experiences. Each also weaves in practical tools, coaching examples, and words of wisdom. And each includes additional exercises you can use to deepen your learning and practice the concepts and skills presented in the chapter.

We want you to imagine taking this journey as if we are linking arms, walking side by side with you as we guide you on the path. It is our greatest honor to support and love you every step of the way.

Note to caregivers: While this book is designed for patients and survivors, we have also worked with hundreds of caregivers. As a caregiver, you will take your own cancer journey with your beloved, or client or patient or parent. But that's a different book, one we plan to write another day. In the meantime, this book will help you recognize what they are going through at every stage and phase. We hope you find comfort and support in these pages.

The Journey is Different for Everyone

Regardless of what the stages and phases on the map are called or how straightforward they may appear on paper, know that your journey isn't going to look exactly like anyone else's. No two people's lives are the same. Perhaps your circumstances, financial or otherwise, may feel at odds with those of the people whose stories you read. Perhaps your Pit experience, or some other stage of the roadmap, won't look exactly the same as Shariann or Keri's, or anyone else's. But we believe that if you look for the similarities, rather than dwelling on the differences, you will see that the feelings and realizations beneath the stories and stages are ones we all share. So, while you will have your own unique version of the Cancer Journey Roadmap experience, it's important to remember we are all traveling the same path.

This is all to say that your stages on the map will have their own flavors and textures and they will be unique to you. But, based on our experience, you will, most likely, go through these stages. And, even though you might want to or try to, you can't skip over any of them. We know this, not only from working with clients, but from first-hand, personal experience. But we are not here to tell you exactly what your journey will look like nor how you will feel. Our hope is that by being able to recognize yourself in any one of the stages or scenarios, and by hearing from others who have gone before you, you will find solace, insight, and ultimately, not only a deeper sense of peace but also a greater sense of freedom. This journey leads to Breakthrough and Transformation, and this is true no matter what your prognosis.

It's also important to know that The Cancer Journey Roadmap is rarely followed in a linear fashion. For example, it's common to swing back and forth between Allies and The Pit (a couple or few times), or to end up back in Initiation when a new protocol is introduced. It's also possible that your treatment is or will become ongoing, well into the Transformation Stage.

As you travel the map, one thing to keep in mind is to try not to speed through it. All stages are equally important, and all offer you gifts and support. We want to remind you that wherever you are, you are exactly where you need to be.

Most importantly, you are not alone. Depending on your perspective and your situation, you may feel as if you don't have many choices or much support. That said, in our experience we have found that most of us have more choices and more available sources of support than we, at first, imagine. As you travel the different stages of your cancer journey, becoming more aware, you will also discover that you are stronger than you thought. We are here to remind you of that and to offer our love and blessings along the way.

Thank you for opening this book. Welcome to The Call of Cancer. We wish you a beautiful journey.

CHAPTER ONE
THE INNOCENCE STAGE

CONVENTIONAL WISDOM: Innocence is weakness. It means you're naïve and people can take advantage of you.

CANCER JOURNEY INSTITUTE WISDOM: When fully embraced, Innocence has the power to reveal our deepest dreams and point us in the direction of our greatest truths.

"Innocence tinctures all things with the brightest hues."
—EDWARD COUNSEL

Innocence: A Time of Loss and a Time of Hope

This chapter will show you how Innocence can help you turn a cancer journey into a profound adventure, fueled by heart-centered dreams and irrepressible hope. We look at Innocence—the loss of it, as we sense the darkness of cancer fall across our lives. And the reclaiming of it, as cancer serves as a wake-up call to reignite our youthful ability to dream big. You will also learn about the importance of your True Values versus Should Values.

Shariann's Story: This Lump Is Growing Legs

It's a Saturday morning in August. I am 38 years old, and my husband and I are driving to San Geronimo State Park for a weekend of camping with friends. As the city and its workday recede, the stresses ease in my psyche. We pass through the town of San Anselmo, and I take comfort in the familiar sights and pine fragrance of the nearby redwoods. Soon, we will be surrounded by the nurturing expanse of towering red tree trunks and fragrant green pine needles.

As we drive along, my hand touches the lump on my neck. A wave of fear surges through my body and tears start to spring. My fingers do a gentle dance on the lump as if to measure its circumference, and I gasp for breath as tears stream down my cheeks. "I think it's growing legs," I say to my husband not daring to turn from the window, trying to control the terror in my soul. I don't want him to see the panic I know must be all over my face.

"What?" he replies.

"I think the lump is growing legs," I repeat, this time turning my head to him. He glances over, sees the tears, and I feel the panic rise in him too.

His voice is loud and panic sounding, he demands, "What do you want to do?!? Do you want to see a doctor right now? On a Saturday!?"

"When we get home," I tell him quietly. "I'll call the doctor then."

You're not truly on the Cancer Journey Roadmap until you sense that your innocence, that take-it-for-granted feeling that life will simply go on as usual, is about to end. You might find a lump, have a pain, prolonged fatigue, or your doctor tells you something is not quite right. This is the moment when a possibility that wasn't anywhere in your thoughts before, is now front and center: Something might be seriously wrong. And, as you read this, the moment is likely now in your past, it isn't a time you will ever forget. Almost overnight, you sense your life is going to be irrevocably altered.

Shariann's Story: A Week After Her Camping Trip, Shariann Receives A Call

"Hi Shariann, this is Dr. Epremian. I have the results from your lab work and it's inconclusive. I'd like you to come back into our office and we can talk about our next steps. I'd like to do a biopsy on your lump to see what's going on. It might be nothing and I want to make sure that it's not cancer. I'll put you through to the receptionist to make an appointment."

I reach for my Palm Pilot to check my calendar, and I lose my grip. I watch with odd detachment as the strange slow-motion scene unfolds. The device almost floats to the ground and then shatters to pieces, my life along with it. "I'll never be able to put it back together. Cancer. No." I say to myself with rising alarm. I numbly gather my briefcase and materials. I cannot take the deep breath I so desperately need. "Breathe!" I command myself.

Cancer has a way of shattering our security and innocence as dramatically as Shariann's Palm Pilot smashed into pieces. This is how it begins, with the "knowing" that the path you've been on is about to disappear, and your life is going to change. It's not yet certain. It's not a sure thing. But you sense a foreshadowing and foreboding, like when they play scary music in a movie, and you feel yourself gripping the edge of your seat with dread. This is the loss of a certain kind of innocence. The innocence that had you believing that something like cancer will never be part of your story.

But there's also another form of innocence, one that you can reclaim and use as a touchstone for how you rebuild and transform your life through the journey of cancer. And the truth is, it often takes the loss of one kind of innocence to regain the other.

We want you to know that in the loss of innocence, in the loss of that naïve belief that you will live forever, a former part of you begins to stir: the magical, dreaming, childlike self that you mostly lose touch with as you grow up and the demands of life and work take over.

There is a hidden gift in this reconnection with your magical childlike self and it will be revealed as you move further along on the roadmap. For now, know that recovering the wholeness of you lies in the remembering of the bigger dreams for your life.

While cancer is no-one's choice for a wake-up call, it offers you a chance to reconnect to your innocence: the dream of why you are here and what your heart truly desires. And while this may not feel tangible at this point, the moment you get the feeling that something isn't quite right, you know deep inside something is about to change. Cancer has a way of interrupting the ho-hum routine you might find yourself falling into—in relationships, work, child rearing—the living of life. And even if your life doesn't feel remotely ho hum, trust us—more will be revealed.

This next section is about retrieving the second kind of Innocence. The kind of Innocence, that once truly grasped, will transform your cancer journey into a path of self-discovery.

Awakening Begins to Dawn in Innocence

Shariann's Story: This Is Not My Beautiful Life

"This is just a stop along the way," I say when I think about my job. It's not my end goal or purpose. It's the job I have for now. What I don't know is "THE" job or career—the one that feels like a passion.

This job feels temporary and unfulfilling. It's a good job, working at a software company and I do it well, as my compensation package shows. I never thought I would be in sales—let's be accurate—account management, but I am a "star performer" and have my own team. So why am I unhappy and restless? When I get quiet, I can feel the unease inside of me. So, I don't slow down or get quiet very often. I just stay busy and distracted. You can call me a Classic Type A.

I have a sweet husband and two brilliant children. Yes, a boy and a girl. I am living the American Dream, and we are the Norman Rockwell picture of family dinners and a warm cozy house, right? Yet, why don't I feel fulfilled? What is wrong with me?

The truth is I'm not completely satisfied with my job, marriage, or my life. Something is missing. I can't put my finger on it, but I know I can't continue this way. I need to DO something different, but what?

Long before she received her diagnosis, Shariann was pursuing her version of the "American Dream." And yet, deep inside, a feeling of dissatisfaction lurked just beneath the surface. In time, she came to realize the dreams she had were the dreams she thought she should have. She didn't feel they were her dreams, but they drove her forward, nonetheless. And with no permission to stop, let alone change course, it took a cancer diagnosis to get her attention.

Like Shariann, our clients at The Cancer Journey Institute are going through the motions, ignoring their true selves at one level or another, before they get their diagnosis. Many, again like Shariann, didn't even know they were settling for an okay life, rather than a truly rewarding one. But, on some level, in some way, all of us were settling or tolerating a life that wasn't honoring the whole of us. Then cancer hits, and it wakes us up like a bucket of ice-cold water.

It is so easy to go unconscious with our daily routine that we don't even notice we're on a treadmill. Between needing to earn a living, not wanting to rock the boat, and rushing around handling the details of our lives, that's entirely understandable. But we are here to tell you, when the hint of a diagnosis shatters your sense of security, it also cracks your heart wide open. It opens you up to possibility, to a new life, a life filled with even more love and based on what truly matters to you.

One of our clients, Leslie, put it this way, "I was running on the hamster wheel of Corporate America and doing whatever it took to make more money and get promoted. I had lost touch with who I was and what I really wanted." Another client, Julie says, I felt that I had no choice but to muscle through my days

"But wait just a darn minute!" You might say, "I wasn't being complacent! I had a beautiful life before diagnosis. I can't see anything I would change!" That was how Keri felt.

Keri's Story: I Don't Need a Wake-up Call

I've got to remember to pack my long johns, I think as I step out of the shower. I finish packing, excited to get in the car and drive to Lake Tahoe for my "girl's" ski trip. Digging through my drawer, my arm brushes the underside of my breast and I feel something hard and foreign. Shit.

I race to my husband for confirmation, "Can you feel a lump here?"

He takes a slow minute and says, "I'm not sure."

I am. But whatever it is, it can wait because there is no way in hell I am going to miss this trip.

I manage to push it out of my mind, start my drive up to Lake Tahoe and sing loudly and freely with the songs on the radio. Trying to distract myself, as the thought of the lump keeps resurfacing, I do a little self-talk, "My life is fantastic. I am passionate about my work, and here I am on my way to something else I adore. I sure as hell don't need any kind of wake-up call."

The flavor of Keri and Shariann's Innocence stories is a little different. Keri thought she had the perfect life. Shariann sensed something missing in hers. But from our experience, whether in big ways or small ones, whether we know it or not, we are all settling for something less than "amazing" at this stage of our journey. In other words, something about our life doesn't light up our souls.

We want to remind you of something we said in the Introduction. Cancer is not a punishment. It is not a cruel response to something you did or didn't do. So right here, feel the truth of that. You didn't bring it on because you are a bad person. But it is a wake-up call, if you allow it to be. And whether your life has been about settling, thriving, or driving yourself so fast you can't stop to listen, there is a way of taking this journey as one of discovery. No matter what your circumstances are, it begins with the opportunity to expand your capacity for self-love and acceptance. And who doesn't want that?

Reclaiming your Innocence

We want to talk more about your innocence because it's an important part of you. We are not talking about the kind of childlike fantasy-driven innocence that promises if you do the right things and don't make waves, you'll never get sick. Thinking you can control whether you get cancer by "doing things right" is like the flip side of the argument that says, if you have cancer, it means you did something wrong. Blaming yourself is not at all helpful. A cancer journey changes that kind of thinking, and that is a good thing.

We are much more interested in what we call a truer innocence. This is different from naivety; it is the beautiful innocence that's inside of you. This is the innocence that connects you to your wondrous imagination. It remembers how to dream and play and savor life. And it has the power to imagine beyond your current situation and limitations without judging your dreams as unrealistic or unacceptable. It's Shariann as a little girl, wrapped in a dream of being a teacher, or later, a writer. The essence of these innocent dreams is potent and never leaves us. And they never left Shariann.

Shariann's Story: I Want to Make a Difference

One of my favorite playtime activities when I was around seven years old was "playing school." I would line up my stuffed animals, the chocolate-colored skinned Eskimo baby doll with a black fur coat given to me by my grandmother; Lamb Chop of the puppeteer Shari Lewis' fame and my namesake; the glamorously lip-sticked girl doll pajama bag made by Aunty Meg; and a bevy of other treasured stuffed companions.

I lined them up on my bed, which was pushed up against the wall and made the perfect stage for my class. They sat ever so erect and ready for whatever I had to share or teach them that day. And, when my students were sad or unruly, I would hold them and let them know that everything would be okay.

This is such a solid memory in my mind. I played it over and over again, joyful in being able to share my knowledge and grow my little students. As I reflect back on this memory, I can see this young child who cared for her little companions. I loved them. I had so much love to give and was not really sure whom I could give it to. These stuffed animals were safe to love.

Growing up in a traditional Asian family, we didn't express emotions—especially love and affection easily. So, this was a safe place to share my abundant, overflowing of love.

Fast forward to age 18 years old. There was an ache or itch inside. Something wanted to be said, but I didn't know what it was. Visions of writing a "self-help book" swirled around in my head. "What would I write about?" High school angst? Peer Pressure? Being Popular vs Being a Wallflower? There were ideas, but not a strong enough voice and definitely not enough confidence to put words to paper. Yet, there was a strong desire to share. The knowing that I had a book in me, that one day I would have something to say, was planted. The underlying message is clear in hindsight, I want to make a difference in the world.

Keri has a similar childhood story that connects to her present-day dreams and how cancer brought them to light.

Keri's Story: I Want To Create Loving Space

When I was a little girl, one of my favorite games (besides putting on shows) was to gather my stuffed animals and escape to the tall grass that grew almost waist-high in the lot beyond our back yard. I loved it because all I had to do to make a nest for my "babies" was stamp the grass down in a circle. There I would curl up with my animals and pretend I was in the wild making them feel safe, loved, and nurtured. I would play there for hours, feeding them snacks and caring for their stuffed animal needs.

You wouldn't think that making nests in the tall grass for stuffed animals could lead to a career but looking back I can see how it eventually evolved into creating safe loving space for the people in my life, including my clients, which has basically been at the core of my career for more than three decades.

Raw Innocence, tempered with life experience, becomes wisdom.

Innocence is not just something you lose and then it's gone forever. Innocence is a part of you, and it can become your superpower if you cultivate it. It's what allows you to become wise. Raw Innocence, tempered with life experience, becomes wisdom. When the child in you can meet the wise adult, who has faced their own mortality and knows in their bones the gift of life, then magic happens, and lives are changed.

"But," you may say, "I have cancer! I don't have time for all this airy-fairy dreamy go back-to-my-childhood kind of stuff!" We get it. All this talk of dreams and innocence might seem like a waste of time right now. After all, cancer is all too real, and shouldn't we just face up to the facts. We won't argue that point, because it is real, and we do have to face it.

This is the chapter of the book you may want to return to when the dust has settled a bit. But do return because claiming your innocence is essential and dreaming is an enormous gift. And, you don't have to do it all at once.

Innocence And Dreaming

Why is all of this so important? Because your dreams allow you to connect to the future, a future that acts as a beacon, helping you get through treatment by imagining a fulfilling life beyond it. As you can see from both Keri and Shariann's stories, dreaming came from their true essences, the unfettered innocence they had as children. And we want you to know that you have this part of you, too. Dreaming helps you to know that while you may have lost your naiveté, something that appropriately happens as you mature, and absolutely happens when you get diagnosed with cancer, you have not lost who you are in the depth of your being. On the contrary, as your naive innocence fades beneath the darkness of cancer, the light of your own innocent dreamer gets re-sparked.

That spark doesn't always have to come by way of a big dream or even an intentional dream-fest. Don't be concerned if you can't seem to get your arms around a "big dream" for yourself, or you're having trouble imagining beyond getting through treatment. Dreaming can be sparked by something as simple as seeing desired future possibilities of your vibrant fitness in a jogger running by; or a deep connection with a significant other when glancing at the couple sitting next to you holding hands across the table; or the passion for your life ignited by watching an enthusiastic TedTalk speaker. These sparks and glimpses of hope find their genesis in Innocence.

Let's explore how we can get to the core of what we want from a dream in this coaching interaction with Marcus (the client) and Shelly (one of our Cancer Journey Coaches):

Coaching Interaction

Marcus: I've secretly wanted to be a rock and roll singer

CJC Shelly: Great. What's stopped you?

Marcus: Are you kidding? I don't think I'm good enough for that. I'm really just a shower and car singer.

CJC Shelly: So, you have a love for singing.

Marcus: Yes, and sometimes I imagine that I'm on American Idol or The Voice and the crowd is cheering and applauding. I could be the sleeper star who gets up there and surprises everybody with my beautiful voice.

CJC Shelly: I get it. You have a desire to bring beauty and joy to a large group of people. You want to be seen in your true talent and beauty.

Marcus: Yes and I want to be successful and make lots of money.

CJC Shelly: Okay, and you want to be recognized and valued for what you do—for your gifts. Does this sound right? How does all this feel?

Marcus: Yeah, you got to the core of it, and you make it sound so simple, but it's not. It's ridiculous. I'm never going to be on American Idol or The Voice and it's too much work. Where would I even start?

CJC Shelly: Here's what I see. You may not get the exact picture or form of what you envision: American Idol/The Voice and being the sleeper star. But you can still have the experience or function of what you want from this secret dream. You can find other ways to bring beauty and joy to a large group and to be seen in your true beauty, whether that is you singing or doing something else that you love. You can still be recognized and valued for your gifts and your work. How would you feel if you could have that in your life?

Marcus: If I had that, it sounds like I would be living my dream.

In this short example, Marcus cannot enjoy the possibility of having what he wants because of a judging inner voice that tells him his dreams are ridiculous. In Innocence, however, you do not need to figure out the how. You do not have to worry about whether you are being realistic or not. You just need to get clear on the what, even though the dream may come to fruition in a very different form than you can imagine right now. What is important is connecting to your true desire.

The spaciousness in Innocence gives you the time to simply explore what you want. This is why we want you to come back to this chapter, time and again. We want you to give this to yourself. It's a gift to listen to what your heart desires and what your soul yearns for.

Innocence Connects Us to Our True Values

Your innocence is your North Star because it springs from your truer self. It is what will help you discover what is most important and what your heart desires most. So, it's not only necessary and helpful with dreaming, but it also helps you to get clear about your values.

Values are the principles or ideals you hold most dear. They serve as your inner compass, by giving you a sense of what feels right, what feels wrong, and what you need in order to be happy. And, when you know what your personal values are, you can consciously honor them. This makes you feel clear-headed and grounded, satisfied and at peace. All of which can really come in handy on a cancer journey.

True Values vs. Should Values

Until she got cancer, Shariann believed that she had a value called, "money." She thought the more money she made, the better person she would be. If you look more closely, though, you can see that she was just doing what her parents expected of a "good Chinese girl." The true reason she wanted to make money was so she could take better care of her family. But it wasn't until she had cancer that Shariann realized that her number one value is Family. That was a big reason that the path she was on initially didn't feel like her own. She was actually honoring her value of family by "busting her hump" to support them. But she was honoring values she thought she should honor versus the ones that would truly make her happy, and she was moving too fast to notice.

But Shariann's innocence was still alive and well. Her dream of teaching her stuffed toys matured to include a desire to communicate a message and make a difference shaping the world's conversation. These are all clues for a compelling vision, with her value of making a difference leading the way.

For Keri, remembering her childlike need to nurture, put her in touch with her value of spirituality—not only loving others, but being loved as well.

Knowing what you truly value is important because honoring them is what will contribute to your peace and happiness. Being clear about your values also helps when you have to make important decisions and choices, especially life-altering ones like what to do about treatment. Please don't stress if you feel like you don't know exactly what your true values are just yet. We can assure you they are there, awaiting your discovery. And they are just one of the many inner resources you can call upon.

We have an extensive exercise at the end of the Allies chapter but let's take a moment to tap into your Innocence to find out what's genuinely important to you. Start with who you were as a child.

- What did you love to do most?

- When were you most happy?

- What did you dream about being or doing?

- What did you do naturally, just because you liked doing it? (Like teaching toys or building nests!)

Answering these questions, and exploring your answers, will lead to discovering your true values.

If we take a moment to look at what brought Shariann joy as a child, we can see the connection to her true values: her family of stuffed animals that she could love and keep safe translates to her true value of Family (not money). Keri's joy in nurturing and caring for her stuffed animals translates to her true value of Love—giving and receiving of love. Your true value is deep in your heart before anyone told you what you "should" want.

Innocence Connects you with your Desired Future

Answering even a few of the questions we just posed, will connect you with a spark of what brings you joy, and that's enough for right now. Also know that small sparks light the way to seeing what is possible. These possibilities combine to create the essence of a compelling vision for your future. A compelling vision means you sense a future that is filled with true desire, hope, joy, meaning and wonder. This kind of vision isn't the five-year goal plan we have been taught to create—filled with pragmatism and "shoulds." It comes from deep within your heart and soul. A compelling vision is much more about feeling these essences rather than having a specific picture or having it all figured out.

Connecting with the soul-driven "what" of your future without the "how" is pivotal in your cancer journey because it will give you courage to move forward. Courage to trust that, while cancer forces you to undergo so much, it can also bring you back to your true essence. For both Shariann and Keri, cancer connected them with the innocent part of themselves. Only their innocence could retrieve their dreams from where they'd been buried deep inside their hearts.

Cancer makes your innocence more accessible because the journey strips you of your will and ability to perform and pretend and returns you to your realness. You need your innocence (imagination and realness) in order to dream, to grow, to change and evolve. You need this part of yourself to transform the tough and challenging journey you are embarked upon into something more authentic and meaningful, and yes, even joyful.

The more you nurture your innocence, the more grounded you will be in facing the unknown with a sense of adventure and curiosity, rather than a sense of fear, "I don't know what I don't know... and isn't that mysterious? Let's go!" Cultivating innocence allows you to remain open to receiving messages and gifts from the Divine. If you are in fear, you are more constricted than receptive—a concept we will talk about more in depth in the Initiation and The Pit Stage chapters. But understand this for now: when fear stories run your thoughts, your powerful imagination is used up creating fear stories rather than dreaming dreams. By cultivating and nurturing your innocence you will focus that same powerful energy on the dreams that will seed and feed your future instead.

This does not mean you live in fantasy or that you should deny what's in front of you. The reality you confront will take both strength and stamina. If you continue to cultivate your powers to direct your imagination and exercise choice, you will discover so many gifts along the way.

You'll know what you need to know when you need to know it.

The bottom line is this: The truth lies within you. And there is power in your innocence. Sometimes the truth of who you really are will get covered up by overwhelm, fear, urgency and noise that unfortunately come with a cancer journey. But if you are willing to get quiet, trust and be patient, you will discover what you need and what's right for you. You'll know what you need to know when you need to know it. And your innocence knows that, too.

Whether you were completely shocked by your diagnosis or you felt it coming a mile away, you will get the gift of transformation. You will be transformed by cancer. And if you trust your innocence, you can also trust that the truth is inside of you. Like Dorothy's shoes in the Wizard of Oz, they were magical and powerful all along, but she didn't know they were until she completed her journey. We are pointing out your ruby slippers super-power at the get go. Don't worry if you can't feel it just yet. Your job is to accept this journey. Ours is to remind you of who you truly are.

ADDITIONAL EXERCISES

Reviewing your Life Before Cancer

The following journal exercise will help you recall and capture the quality of your life, before you were diagnosed. In other words, how was life before cancer? Understanding this will be helpful when you look back to Innocence from the perspective of Transformation. It will allow you to track the changes you have made and growth you have experienced throughout your cancer journey.

Here are some writing prompts. Set a timer for 20 minutes and allow yourself to free write, which means simply put the pen to your paper, or your fingers to the keyboard, and allow your thoughts to flow onto the page without editing, second-guessing, or stopping. After 20-minutes, if there is more flowing through you, set the timer for another 20-minutes. Stop when the timer goes off.

Writing prompts:

1. What was happening in your life—describe a typical day?
2. What did you dream about? What were your hopes for the future?
3. What were you tolerating? This might take a few moments to connect to because the things that we "tolerate" become the norm like background noise. For example, I always sleep on my right side because my left shoulder hurts; my husband doesn't talk to me when he comes home from work, but it's okay because I know he's tired; my boss is disrespectful lots of the time, but I just ignore it.
4. What did you dream about doing "someday" when everything—money, time, situations, etc. lined up?

Allow these writings to rest. If you find you have more to add later, you can. We will revisit these writings in Transformation.

Remembering Joyful Childhood Moments

There are clues to what your heart and soul desire. They show up in playful moments you had when you were a child. Use the journaling prompts below, setting the timer for 20 minutes, like the exercise above.

Writing Prompts:

1. What were you doing when you lost track of time?
2. What was your favorite game?
3. How did you entertain yourself when you were alone?
4. What do you remember doing, or what people said you did when you thought no one was watching? (e.g., Dancing in the living room, making movies, building structures with blocks or Legos, experimenting in the kitchen)

Allow your writings to marinate. Continue to add to them, as and when you want, when you remember things. You don't need to re-read them now. We'll come back to them in Transformation.

CHAPTER TWO
THE CALL STAGE

CONVENTIONAL WISDOM: Cancer is a battle. I am being called to fight. This is happening to me because bad things always do.

CANCER JOURNEY INSTITUTE WISDOM: Cancer is a transformational journey. I am being called to grow and change.

"Life is what happens while you're busy making other plans."
—JOHN LENNON

The Call: The Journey Begins in Earnest

Once you hear the words "you have cancer," you have heard The Call. In this chapter, we introduce you to the importance of slowing down and becoming present to yourself. We teach you how to be in the moment, even amid the fear and chaos of a recent cancer diagnosis. You will also learn how this stage can trigger "fight, flight or freeze" responses that awaken your inner energies of Victim and Warrior. Exploring these archetypes, we'll show you how to work with them in empowering ways.

Shariann's story: My first Lymphoma Diagnosis

"I think the hardest part is the waiting," I say to my husband after finishing up my biopsy procedure. I don't know which one of us is more nervous. We've been told that my doctor would call the next day with the results. The "waiting game" begins.

Tossing and turning in bed, I feel every muscle in my body tense and then attempt to release. My mind spins, prays and bargains, "Please, God, let it just be nothing. I promise that I'll be good from now on. I'll eat right. I'll exercise. I'll think good thoughts. Whatever it takes! Please!" My soul reaches out to anyone, any entity who can hear my cries. Turning my face to my pillow, I whisper, "Please, I don't want it to be anything bad. And then another voice enters, my warrior voice, the voice that is ready to fight off any threat, any fear, "It's nothing," my warrior says. "Remember, other people in our family have had lumps that were nothing. It's just your turn. Stop being dramatic. Deal."

The poor night's sleep makes for a weary day, but I keep busy, striving to distract myself. Work calls, miscellaneous tasks, and idle chitchat with colleagues. Meanwhile, my mind swirls. Almost as a reflex, I touch the bandage on my neck. I keep looking at my watch wondering when the doctor's office will call.

It's 6pm and my cell phone rings. I excuse myself from the kitchen table and enter the empty, unlit dining room to take the call. Encased in darkness, I answer with a cautious, "Hello?"

"It's Dr. Richards, Shariann, and I have the results from your biopsy. Pathology shows that you have Hodgkin's Lymphoma—class B," he says clinically.

"Lymphoma? What is that?" I ask.

"Shariann, you have cancer of the lymph nodes," he replies. His voice sounds flat and far away. In an instant my head is buzzing, and my ears have grown muffs. I can barely hear over the pounding in my chest. I have left my body. Someone, the woman on the chair in the dining room is having a conversation, but another part of me is hovering above in suspended animation. My world has stopped.

I manage to hang up the phone and trance-walk to the doorway of the kitchen. My eyes meet my mother's, who is now looking up from her bowl of rice and meats, chopsticks suspended in mid-air. I can barely get the words out, my throat closes, trying to keep in the tears, but to no avail. Overtaken by body shaking sobs, I manage to croak, "I have cancer."

My mom rushes over, catching me before I hit the ground. In her arms, I let myself collapse. I feel like a child. My life has just exploded, and I sob because there is nothing else to do.

I had no idea this would be the first of four cancer journeys with lymphoma. All I knew in that moment was a sense of unreality as my former life and all my dreams seemed to die. This can't be happening! Will I make it? I can't hear anything. I can't think. Cancer of the blood?! What does that even mean? What do I do? I'm too busy to have cancer! What is the treatment for this? Will I need chemo? Will I lose my hair? My kids are too young to lose their mom! In and amongst the loud roaring in my ears, these thoughts speed through my mind. Little did I know that the shock and paralysis would take weeks and months to subside. Cancer. I have cancer.

The Call is the stage when cancer knowingly enters your life. It can begin as a face-to-face meeting with your primary care doctor, surgeon, or oncologist. It can begin, as Shariann's did, with a phone call. Whoever the messenger, and however the message is delivered, when you hear the statement, "You have cancer," you have heard The Call. When this happens, the bubble of Innocence pops so hard you can almost hear the snap. At that moment, you shut down, go numb. You may even have an out-of-body experience. Shariann describes a roaring in her ears. David puts it this way: "My ears shut down as the doctor's mouth continued to move." Karen describes a floaty feeling, "as if [my feet] floated above the floor."

Panic sets in almost immediately. Your brain fills with scary thoughts and fear stories. It's a bit like a horror movie, only much more real. What if…" scenarios will likely blow through your mind. "What if I lose my hair? What if I can't work? *Am I going to die?*"

Here's what Keri experienced.

Keri's Story: A Rare Form of Breast Cancer

Sitting in the cramped hallway of the ER, my husband and I wait for his name to be called for an X-ray. His ribs are most likely broken from a freak fall in our driveway. The poor thing, he's in so much pain, I think as I settle in for what I know might be a long wait. My phone vibrates and I recognize the number—it's coming from the same building as a matter of fact. Shit.

I've been waiting for weeks since my lumpectomy to get the "all clear." The biopsy didn't show any cancer, but they sent it off to pathology just to be sure. We'd returned from Maui just a few days ago, and my surgeon said she'd email me when the results came in. I still hadn't heard anything. "No news is … no news," I kept telling myself. I managed to keep myself sane with this mantra during these weeks of being in limbo.

I've stopped breathing and my pulse rises in my ears as I answer my phone. She would only be calling for one reason and I might as well get the news now. "Can you talk?" she asks. I say yes even though I'm sitting in the ER. Everything in me says I need to hear what she has to say. "They're saying it's a rare kind of breast cancer."

After that, I remember nothing of what she says. I leave my body. Snippets of conversation zoom in while I zoom out: Radiation… chemotherapy… plastic surgeon… oncology… I feel like I'm in an echo chamber. Nothing is connecting. Nothing makes sense.

"…So, does that make sense, then?" She asks. I'm having trouble taking it all in, and I say so. "Well, you SAID you could TALK!" my surgeon replies sternly. She doesn't exactly have a bedside manner. Somehow, I get off the phone with an appointment to see a plastic surgeon and "discuss my options." None of this makes any sense to me. It's completely unreal. I am a zombie.

My husband comes out of his x-ray procedure, and they tell us he's broken two ribs. I'm not there. This is about him right now though, right? So, I get up, car keys in hand and step through my fog and haze into the parking lot. I'm so overwhelmed; I nearly collapse as we get to the car. I can barely get the words out, "They say I have breast cancer…" I'm crying now. My husband does the best he can to hold me. I've said it out loud. Oh, God! What do I DO?!

Yes, you have cancer.
But everything else is still an unknown.
So, breathe, and just let that in.

Keri's mind and body went into shock, a result of being presented with more devastating information than she could possibly process. But the shock also numbed her momentarily to the scary imaginings her mind had already started making up.

Everybody runs worst-case scenarios when disaster hits. It's how your brain is programmed. But you need to know this: most of the stories your mind is making up are not true. In fact, in the moment of first learning of your diagnosis, none of them are. Yes, you have cancer. But everything else is still an unknown. So, breathe, and just let that in.

It's true you are being called onto a new path and your life is on a new trajectory. You have received a diagnosis and it feels like a blow. The rest, as we've said, is yet to be determined. And that's exactly as it needs to be in this moment. It's also where *you* need to be—in this moment.

As with any stage of this journey, there are knowns and unknowns, things you can control and things you cannot. In the Innocence stage, the power lies in your willingness and ability to dream. In The Call stage, your power is most accessible when you are your clearest and most grounded self. And that self is only available to you if you can remain rooted in the present moment or what Eckhart Tolle famously calls, "The Power of Now."

Being present in the moment can be a real challenge when your mind is spinning with the news of your diagnosis. Try to be gentle with yourself. Recognize that you cannot see into the future or know what lies ahead. Clarity is only available to you in the here and now. More knowledge will come when it's needed. You can trust that. Meanwhile, you're still here, we're right beside you. And you're still you.

We're going to help you by telling you more of what you can expect, but first let's get clear about where you are.

Your mind is probably numb, drumming up worst-case scenarios or making future plans for future circumstances that may never occur. This is completely human and normal. And, as we said earlier, it's also part of your biology because your mind is designed to perceive and anticipate threats. So, it's really good at making up scary stories.

Now would be a good time for us to pause together. You've just received a huge shock. You may be thinking, "You've got to be kidding me! How am I supposed to stop future-tripping and get present when so many thoughts and fears are moving through me?" We understand. That's why we're going to share a coaching interaction between JoAnn, who has just received a cancer diagnosis, and her Cancer Journey Coach (CJC) Mary. Perhaps you can recognize yourself in JoAnn.

Coaching Interaction

JoAnn: I've been diagnosed with cancer, and I cannot get past the shock.

CJC Mary: I get it. Shock is a good coping mechanism initially so let's try and get into the present moment where your power is.

Joann: I know…but I'm just so scared about it all, that I can't even consciously take a step forward.

CJC Mary: Okay, so I hear you are scared. That's a first step. Let's just be with your scared feeling. Where are you feeling scared in your body?

Joann: It's this buzz or something in my chest like I'm anticipating the worst that can happen. I keep thinking that my life is over.

CJC Mary: Mmmm…I feel the buzz and it also feels like you're amping up, like your nerves are being triggered.

Joann: Exactly. If my life is over, what about EVERYTHING! My family, my work, my plans? What type of treatment will I go through? Will I be able to handle it? I hate needles!

CJC Mary: So, JoAnn, let's slow this down. Notice the energy coursing through you now. Do you feel it? It feels frenetic and swirly to me. What are you noticing?

Joann: It feels like an adrenaline or panic surge. Argh!!! Help me!!

CJC Mary: I got you. You're not alone in this. Let's take a deep breath through your nose and then slowly out through your mouth.

Joann: (Takes a Deep Breath)

CJC Mary: Good, now take another one, even slower.

Joann: (Slowing down her pace. Breathes in and out.)

CJC Mary: Good. Now take one more and this time, when you exhale, make a sound.

Joann: (Takes a breath in and makes an exaggerated noise on the breath out.)

CJC Mary: How are you doing now?

Joann: Better. I can feel my heartbeat slow down.

CJC Mary: Good. Let's come back to your body. We're going to hold off on the story circling in your mind right now. We can come back to that. For now, drop into your body and tell me what you're feeling.

Joann: I'm calmer. The nervous energy has calmed down. I'm feeling sad, (her voice starts to quiver as she cries.) I really don't want to deal with cancer. I just want someone to make it all go away.

CJC Mary: I hear you, JoAnn. You didn't ask for this to come into your life. It's a major disruption. (Pause) We're going to take this one step at a time…together.

Joann: Thank you (she speaks through her tears.)

CJC Mary: What's coming up now?

Joann: I can breathe and now want to call my boss and let her know that I'm not coming into work tomorrow. Actually… I want to take off the whole week.

CJC Mary: Well, JoAnn, that sounds like you've reconnected with your power. Will you call your boss after our call and text me that it's done?

Joann: Yes. Wow! That felt freeing to say and allowing myself to do this. Can we reconnect later this week?

CJC Mary: Absolutely. Let me get my schedule.

As you can see from JoAnn's coaching interaction, the most important thing to do in The Call Stage, your only job in fact, is to slow things down and stay as present as you can. It starts with breathing and includes feeling whatever you're feeling, or just letting yourself be numb. Now is not the time to judge or pressure yourself. Nor is it the time to make plans beyond the immediate future or worry about telling people about your diagnosis. You'll do that when you are good and ready. But it is a good moment to breathe, like Mary did with JoAnn. Take as many gentle, nourishing breaths, as you need. And if you find yourself getting out ahead of yourself or filling in the unknown with scary scenarios, press the pause button. And take another deep breath.

Before you move on to the next section, you may also want to take a break. We are great believers in the soothing power of mini-naps, cups of tea, and moments of relaxation. So, while we mention it here, we encourage you to take as many breaks as you need as you read through this book. For the moment, come back when you're ready for more information. We are going to introduce you to two particular aspects of Self that are probably getting activated right about now.

Meet the Victim and the Warrior

We have found that a significant percentage of our clients respond to the Call stage in one of two ways: Victim or Warrior. And most of us swing back and forth between the two.

It's helpful to know about these parts of yourself because we have found that if you can dance with the Warrior and Victim energies in an open, non-judgmental way, you are opening to the kind of awareness that can make cancer a journey of transformation. To achieve this kind of awareness, you will need to slow down *enough* and get present *enough* to stop reacting to everything that is going on. We know this isn't an easy feat. Let's take a deep breath here together.

Cancer is big and scary. So, naturally you will do what we humans have always done when facing something terrifying: you instinctively choose fight, flight, or freeze. These reactions are coded into us, and under stress, out they come. We collapse into Victim (flight) and let out a great wail and cry. Or we power-up as Warriors (fight), determined to beat this thing, and fight like hell. One moment we are in a pool of self-pity, the next we are barking out orders like a military commander, and still next we are numb and completely paralyzed (freeze.)

You will discover space inside of you, away from the fear and chaos, which will allow you to hear the whispers of your soul.

The Call can be a crazy time as you move in and out of numbness, collapse into helplessness (Victim) or keep pushing through (Warrior). These aspects of who you are run deep within. And it will take a conscious effort to root yourself in the here and now in order to befriend them. You can do it, moment by moment. As you learn to take a deep breath and check in with yourself, you will become more and more able to get present. You will discover space inside of you, away from the fear and chaos that will allow you to hear the whispers of your soul. This deep awareness is always available if you're willing to slow down and tune in to yourself. But even if you can't slow down right now, know that it's always there for you—this quiet space, as well as your soul and its whispers.

We want to make something very clear: Nothing is wrong with assuming a Victim or Warrior role. These two archetypes are part of a spectrum of human behaviors. And you, like us, possess both of them. What's also true is that they tend to gain steam and power in the face of a cancer diagnosis. Once you are aware of which of these you have a tendency towards, you can respond in ways that meet your needs. Awareness is first and foremost. The key to accessing that awareness is to recognize how each of these aspects presents themselves in you. So, what are their characteristics and how can you recognize them?

The Victim

Cancer can be a trigger for all the other traumatic events in your life, setting up a chain reaction. You may not only feel like a victim of your cancer diagnosis. This diagnosis can bring up all the other times you have been a victim. This "*proves*" to your Victim self that you have been a victim all along.

Anne Lamott put it so well when she quoted a friend in a TED Talk, "My Inside self has no age, I'm every age I've ever been." In other words, even though we may have been hurt decades ago, it feels like it's happening now. When our Victim self gets triggered, we often feel defeated before we begin. "Why bother?" we ask. "I knew this would happen." "Bad things always seem to happen to me."

What this means is that when you discover you have cancer, you don't just reel from that shock, you may be tapping into all the other times in your life when you felt victimized. The time your father hit you, your parents divorced, you underwent a terrible breakup or lost a dream job. It's a tsunami of hurt, and it tends to come crashing over you, especially if this is your "go to" coping mechanism. One of our clients described it this way, "Even though I was shocked, there was part of me saying, 'Of course this happened to me! How did I screw it up this time?!' And we knew exactly what he meant, because we have felt that way too.

You are feeling your Victim self, but it is only a small portion of who you are.

The Victim takes over so swiftly; you may not even realize it. It's a bit like a body invasion. All at once you are hurting and crying, wishing someone would make it go away. The feelings are not only very human; but they are also so strong and take over so completely you can't step back from them. You only know you want to hide under the bed covers and not deal with anything. Or, you know you are sad and mad and desperately want someone to rescue you. Or, you know you want someone, anyone, to make sense of your pain and take care of you. However, you are unaware that you have stepped into Victim mode.

Sometimes it feels like all you can do is keep talking about how awful things are, hoping desperately that something changes. Believe us, we know how hopeless everything can appear from the Victim perspective.

Just thinking about being a Victim feels vulnerable and powerless. But also know this: while the Victim may have you in its grasp, you're right now giving yourself a little space by being willing to see and get curious about this part of you. From here you can see it a bit more clearly. Breathe into that space… and just for a moment, sense that *you are not only The Victim.* You are feeling your Victim self, but it is only a small portion of who you are.

It's essential to create this psychic space between you and the Victim, because when it is in charge you are so tightly wrapped in your own misery you can't see the help that is right in front of you. You can't feel how valued and cared for you actually are.

So yes, in a very real way you are a victim of cancer. You didn't ask for it, you didn't want it, but you have it. That's the simple truth of your situation. But you are not a Victim with a capital "V." Over the years, we have shown hundreds of our clients the way to be with their Victim energy so they can feel both safe and loved. Now we want to show you, too. Take a deep breath, and, if you feel comfortable doing so, simply wrap your arms around you. Feel how good that feels. We are going to take you on a journey.

Exercise: Embracing the Victim

Imagine for a moment that you have walked into a sparsely furnished room. In one corner a little child sits all alone. As you look at them, you feel their aloneness and helplessness. It is as if they have been waiting there forever for someone to rescue them. You approach slowly, and gaze into their eyes. You are a part of each other and have always been. Very gently, you bend down and take them in your arms. You feel them trembling and their tears soak your shirt. You murmur, "It's all right, dear one. I am here now; I can look after you." You see how small and in need they are. You find your heart opening. You feel compassion for this frightened child and know that you are here to protect them. There is no room for judgment or blame, only love. Hold them for as long as it feels right.

As you embrace and care for this child, you are doing the same to your Victim, which is that scared, young, helpless part of you that needs to be held and reassured. When you embrace your Victim, you transform your relationship to this aspect of yourself. No longer under its control, you see it for what it truly is: a small and frightened child. No wonder it weeps and wails and doesn't have the words it needs to ask for help. No wonder you feel so helpless in its grip.

Here's the truth: Once you open the door to love, it wants nothing more than to flood in.

Taking the Victim in your arms, something extraordinary happens. The relief can be almost instantaneous. You, yourself feel loved and cared for. In opening the door, and your arms to the Victim, you embrace yourself, too. It shifts things. It gives you the ability to feel your pain and fear without completely losing yourself to your Victim feelings. You are learning the amazing capacity to be self-soothing and gentle with yourself.

But please be advised, you don't need to and won't do this perfectly. It's not a once-and-for-all kind of thing. Most of us have to come back, time and again, challenged to remember to have compassion for, and to be less judgmental and less identified with, your Victim self. But as Maya Angelou said, "Do the best you can until you know better. Then when you know better, do better." And, we would add, not a moment before.

The Warrior

Shariann's Story: I Don't Have Time for This Cancer Nonsense!

After the shock of my cancer diagnosis and crying in my mother's arms, I was still in a heart-thumping state of shock. Yet deep in the recesses of my soul, the Warrior summoned me, "You can't stay here in wallow-land. You have a big meeting to-morrow." An immediate rush of adrenaline swept in and shook me awake. I thought, "I am leading the meeting with the head honchos at Schwab! I don't have time for this cancer nonsense! I need to pull myself together!"

The warrior is a fiercely brave and independent part of you that many of us call upon when faced with adversity. Always ready to go into battle, to "fight the good fight," the warrior is the pull-yourself-up-by-the-bootstraps part of you. It says you can and should do whatever it takes to get on with life, get the job done, overcome adversity. And for god's sake, quit whining! The Warrior is the part of you that doesn't want to feel powerless, paralyzed or out of control, even for one mo-ment. In fact, it will do just about anything to avoid these feelings, or any feelings for that matter.

"Let's Fight the Good Fight!" "I'm battling cancer." "F**k cancer!" "I'm going to beat this!" "Stand Up to Cancer!" These battle cries of the

Warrior are strongly reinforced in the cancer world that often portrays cancer as an enemy to be fought. You can feel the energy in the words. You are steeling and shoring up your psyche and body, as if putting on armor. Your expression is firm, and your attention is focused. You are in the war against cancer. And you're going to win it!

Warriors are revered, and that can be detrimental.

Warrior energy definitely has its payoffs. It's attractive because it makes you feel purposeful, in control. You're doing something. You may have been brought to your knees with the diagnosis of cancer, but you are not going to let that take you down. You are readying yourself for whatever is going to come your way. To take the Wonder Woman or Superman stance is to feel invincible. Scary words and emotions bounce off, deflecting fear and overwhelm. You are officially "warrior-ing up." And everyone, seeing you fight back, is keen to let you know how well you're handling things.

Society loves, even reveres, the Warrior. "She is so strong." "I never see him get upset." "You'd never know anything was different." "He never missed a day of work." "She is battling cancer so bravely." The cancer world favors the Warrior over the Victim. The "Ribbon Movements," whether Pink, Teal, Red, Purple, want to encourage "Survival." They promote (with good intentions) the notion that Warriors are more likely to survive than Victims.

This isn't true, but in our society, being a Victim is often seen as something to be ashamed about. Nobody wants to be one, and we'll talk more about that later. The point is, Warriors are revered, and that can be detrimental. Why? Because it feeds the Warriors' tendency to keep proving to themselves and everyone else that they don't need help, that they've "got this." Culturally, we view this as noble. Truthfully though, it's a lonely existence and can also be a huge trap.

No one can hold this stance for the entire journey. It's just not sustainable. Even Warriors get tired. Our bodies, minds, and emotions wear down. And worse still, over time, reaching for the Warrior again and again leads to isolation, resentment, and tremendous fatigue.

Continuing to push through alone, keeping your "guard up," whether physically or emotionally, is not only unsustainable, but it's also what puts us on The Victim-Warrior seesaw. The tired and lonely "I've got this," Warrior, sooner or later becomes the helpless, isolated Victim.

Here's how it works. Exhausted, we feel stuck and engulfed by our own judgments of what we think it means to be a Victim, and eventually we manage to fight our way back to Warrior. But with every tip of the seesaw, we become more and more alone. What's more, this seesaw motion and continuous pushing and gearing up, not to mention isolation, can cause your already challenged immune system untold stress.

"I've got this!" That was Shariann's mantra. Translation: "If I ask for or accept your help it means I'm a Victim. It means I'm weak and I will lose the battle." When you are constantly in Warrior mode it lets others off the hook. Only, does it? Because those who care for you would probably be a lot happier if they could do something for you. But they can't because you are doing it all. Warrior mode also isolates you from the heart-opening joy of receiving and being truly seen and known. And it can cause a lot of hurt to those who feel shut out too. Going through an entire cancer journey as a Warrior cuts you off from other people and the beautiful gifts they want to offer.

We believe that is too great a price to pay.

Let us pause here, because there is also good news. Just as being able to see your Victim opens the door to healing, the same is true when you can see and appreciate your Warrior. Contained within your Warrior Self are your brave heart, your beautiful strength and incredible will. In terms of ability to triumph over circumstances, Warrior leads the way. So, we are not here to take away your fighting spirit. It is an amazing part of your humanity. What we are saying is, the fight doesn't have to be so hard or lonely. You can harness the strength of your Warrior self.

And you (and your team/tribe, we might add) can do it with the most powerful combination available: Your love and your "why?"

A Warrior without a "why" is like a ship without a rudder. "Ready, fire, aim," is the unmoored warrior's cry—ready to fight, but not sure why, or with whom, or for what. Fighting to overcome a challenge, or simply to avoid being a Victim, becomes exhausting pretty quickly. Embracing this as a journey is a mindset that has already opened the door. What we want you to know right now is you can trust that the process is unfolding. What's important to do right now, though, is to embrace your inner Warrior.

Exercise: Embracing the Warrior

Settle into a comfortable chair. We are about to take another journey. This time it is to meet your Warrior Self. Let's start by bringing your focus to your heart area. Breathe in and out slowly and effortlessly, tuning into your heart. Gradually relax until you enter a dream-like state.

Now imagine that you are walking down a long corridor at the end of which your Warrior self awaits. You notice them standing so tall and straight. They are the part of you that has tried so hard to protect you, all of your life. They have helped you to survive and overcome so much. As you approach, you see in their eyes how much this has cost them, how tired they are. And your heart opens. This brave being, who has defended you and acted on your behalf since you can remember, has always had your best interest at heart. And they are a precious part of you.

Thank your Warrior self for all they have done. Tell them you need them more than ever now, but only in a supporting role. You need their courage, not to fight, but to ask for help. You need their strength, not to push through, but to be vulnerable enough to let those around you know what's really going on. You need their loyalty, not to blindly serve everybody else's needs, but to help you take this journey in your own way, remaining true to yourself. Notice your words usher in a deep peace and understanding. There is no need to fight alone. There is no need to fight at all.

When you enroll this new Warrior self into your cancer journey, beautiful things happen. The Warrior becomes an amazing part of your growth and change. As you transform your relationship to this aspect of who you are, you find the courage to do what you have been fighting against all along—to ask for help. Asking for help does not mean you have lost a battle-of-the-wills, or that you are weak or have given up. Quite the contrary. It means you can direct your will more consciously towards your real needs and be even more true to yourself.

Asking others to walk with you on this journey is actually the bravest and most powerful thing you can do.

Making an ally of your Warrior self means you can stop pushing yourself beyond your limits. You can make room in your life for friends and family. You can ask a neighbor to pick up the groceries or the kids from school, your spouse to cook dinner, or someone to simply sit with you while you bawl over a favorite tearjerker movie. You realize that people love to be of service, and that you are so much happier when you are open to receiving. Now you can see and feel that you are not carrying the load alone. Now you can let in the love. We are here to testify—a little willingness goes a long way.

"You're so strong, you can beat this," is meant as praise in today's world. But it doesn't work. And it doesn't stop the hurt or loneliness inside. Your Warrior is tired. You are tired too. It's time to share the burden. For this is what we've learned: Asking others to walk with you on this journey is actually the bravest and most powerful thing you can do.

Blame and Shame

Don't be alarmed if blame, or shame has come into your thoughts and feelings. They are culprits at this stage of the game—very human, but not very helpful. They also play a key role in Warrior and Victim and serve to exacerbate the isolation felt in both. We are going to address them here, so you don't have to be held so tightly in their grips.

Here are some examples of how they can show up. Shariann's fear of weakness (shame) had her push away help. Laurie was convinced that she had caused her lung cancer with the one cigarette she had sneaked in high school and walked around for years blaming herself and being ashamed to the point of rejecting love and support. Marge told no one about her breast cancer diagnosis because she felt shame about it, and certain that everyone would think less of her for what she perceived as a frailty. She needed her work reputation to stay intact. She needed to continue to appear strong and in charge.

Some of us blame ourselves for causing our cancer because we ate poorly, acted incorrectly, or simply because our very existence is somehow wrong. This creates shame that permeates our being and is not subject to logic. It helps to be aware of blame and shame and how they operate, so we can be more at choice. They are isolating and painful because they make us feel separate from those around us, and from ourselves as well. When we recognize this, we can understand how Victim and Warrior are triggered by these feelings.

The Victim and Shame: In Victim, we blame ourselves for getting sick because we harbor a deep sense of shame. Shame is based on a deep-seated belief that there's something wrong with us. We didn't just *do* something wrong; we *are* wrong. Therefore, when "bad" things happen, like cancer, it has to be our fault. This belief comes across in the Victim perspective as: "Of course, this is happening to me. Bad things always happen to me!" What is not being said is, "Because I don't deserve anything better, or I deserve to be punished."

The Victim and Blame: Because your Victim feels helpless, powerless, and undeserving, blaming yourself and others for your situation comes naturally to this part of you. In fact, blaming others feels like a break from blaming yourself. Because your Victim self is so full of shame, and secretly thinks you're at fault, it is almost a relief to put the blame onto others, relieving yourself of all responsibility, momentarily, at least. "If my husband had just stepped up, then I wouldn't be so stressed and I wouldn't have got cancer!" "If my job hadn't demanded that I work round the clock…" "My doctor should have diagnosed me sooner." "I had to…" "I had no choice because they made me do [fill in the blank]." Can you feel the powerlessness and resignation?

The Warrior and Shame: The Warrior equates vulnerability with shame, so they hide behind a façade of strength. They dare people to pity them and will push back hard at the first hint of sympathy. They are quick to bark, and at times, they bite. "I'm fine," they bitterly insist.

The Warrior and Blame: The Warrior who is in blame is a Warrior with a sword in their hand and is dying to use it. They are poised for attack and won't hesitate to strike if you so much as breathe in their direction. "I can handle this, but they keep throwing me curve balls," they accuse. Warriors seem to gain energy from false outrage. The thing to remember is they are doing it all because it's a marvelously distracting numbing device.

Victim, Warrior, blame, shame. They are all parts of our messy, human way of getting through life. They are, after all, coping mechanisms. The trouble is they remove us from the present moment by distracting us with a lot of drama and angst. At first, they feel like brilliant strategies, helping you to avoid your true feelings, which are likely overwhelming right now. But those true feelings will come out eventually. They can only be held back for so long, as you will discover. And rest assured, we will be there to help you deal with them. Until then, when you fall into Victimhood, or find yourself railing at your fate as Warrior, or when you take on blame or shame, take a *pause*. Know that at heart, you are simply trying to protect yourself.

The road may be a little bumpy right now. That's okay. It's still a road. And by taking this book into your hands and heart, you are absolutely on the road to more self-love and compassion. All that we have spoken about so far is part of the journey. And trust us, that is a beautiful thing. You're being called to something greater, to more of you. You don't know what that means just yet. But consider this your wake-up call.

ADDITIONAL EXERCISES

Exercise: Getting Grounded

Shock is a real thing. Combine it with "denial" and it can be a potent coping mechanism for The Call. But it is only a temporary solution—it is not sustainable. So, it's helpful to get grounded and connected with yourself. Here is an exercise you can do to get present and grounded in the current moment, where your true power lives. You will want to set aside at least 5 minutes for this exercise.

1. Start by finding a quiet place to sit and get into a comfortable position.
2. Gently close your eyes and take three deep breaths, making a sound with each exhale.
3. In your mind's eye, imagine sending a grounding cord from your body down into the earth—through the building that you're in, through the crust of the earth, through the layers, to the center of the earth. Allow your grounding cord to wrap around the center of the earth and clip onto the hook with your name on it. Mother Earth knows you. Feel the grounding cord go tight. You are connected and grounded.
4. Notice what you're *hearing* in this moment. Is it the sound of a chirping bird, the fan of the air conditioner or maybe it's the sound of your own breathing?
5. Notice what you *smell* in this moment. Is it the smell of toast from this morning, the smell of your dog sleeping beside you? Or maybe a smell is not available to you in this moment. That's okay too.
6. Notice the *taste* in your mouth in this moment. Is it the peach tea you were sipping, the peanut butter you put on your toast, or nothing but the inside of your mouth?
7. Allow your hands to *touch* what is in front of you or on you. What do you feel? Is it the soft blanket that is resting

on your lap? The cool, smooth surface of your cup of tea? Or maybe the nubby texture of your pants? Notice the texture of what you're feeling.

8. Open your eyes and bring your attention to yourself and the room you are currently in. Take another deep breath and notice what you see in this moment. Look around the room and allow your eyes to land on what's around you. Focus on one object. Simply notice.

9. Take another deep breath and feel your connection to this moment. You are safe, connected, and present. Remain seated and quiet, until you are ready to move on.

10. From this exercise, you notice that your nervous system has calmed, and you are more able to be present to what is going on without being pulled to the future or past. Savor this feeling. You can come back to this grounded space as often as you need.

Exercise:
Journaling: Getting to Know Your Victim and Your Warrior

The more you become familiar with how your Victim and your Warrior operate, the sooner you'll be able to dismount the Victim-Warrior Seesaw. The following exercises will help you discover more about each of them. As the words flow into your journal, don't judge them, or try to pretty them up. Keep in mind, this is between you and you, and the more intimate you become with both your Victim and Warrior, the more you will access your personal power. Here goes.

Victim Rant

1. Get out a piece of paper and pen or prepare your computer with a new screen.

2. Set your timer for 20 minutes, you may not take the whole time, but having space is freeing.

3. Start with one thing that your Victim says, like:
"I can't because …"
"It's not my fault because…"
"It is my fault because…"
"Or whatever your Victim would say."

4. Just let your Victim rant. Keep writing down their rants until they have nothing left to say or what they're saying becomes super repetitive. Reset your timer for 20 more minutes, if you have more to release when it goes off the first time.

Warrior Cry

This exercise is similar to the Victim rant, only this time we're letting the Warrior release.

1. Get out a piece of paper and pen or prepare your computer with a new screen.

2. Set your timer for 20 minutes. Again, you may not take the whole time, but having space is freeing.

3. Start with one thing that your Warrior says, like:
"I don't need any help!"
"It's easier if I just do this myself."
"I need to be strong at all times."
"I can't show any signs of weakness!"
"Nobody gets it anyway…"

4. Just let your Warrior rant. Keep writing down their rants until they have nothing left to say or what they're saying becomes super repetitive. Reset your timer for 20 more minutes, if you have more to release when it goes off.

Becoming more conscious of the rants and cries of your Victim and your Warrior lets you know when they are "in the house." You can return to this exercise whenever you feel the need. These exercises are highly effective because they will increase your awareness of these energies, while also creating a space for them to be seen and heard—which usually quiets them down. We recommend combining these journaling exercises with returning to the *Embracing the Victim* and *Embracing the Warrior* guided visualizations we provided earlier in the chapter.

CHAPTER THREE
THE INITIATION STAGE

CONVENTIONAL WISDOM: Information is power. I should be vigilant and leave no stone unturned.

CANCER JOURNEY INSTITUTE WISDOM: You have both the time and the right to make your own decisions. Keep your power and don't give it away.

"The thing you fear most has no power. Your fear of it is what has the power. Facing the truth really will set you free."
–OPRAH WINFREY

Initiation: Crossing the Threshold into an Unknown World

In Initiation, a period characterized by a steep learning curve, multiple doctor appointments, and pressure to make your treatment choices, is where we show you how to develop the mindset to make the decisions that are right for you. We show you that you have more choice than you think. More power than you know. We also help you distinguish between fear and fear stories, so that you can stay centered and advocate for yourself, no matter what.

Shariann's Story: Entering the Land of Cancer

It's dark outside; night has fallen without my noticing. I'm glued to the computer, reading every tidbit I can find about Hodgkin's Lymphoma and its treatments. A one-inch-thick stack of printouts sits beside me; I cannot stop until I have searched every nook and cranny for information.

There is an insatiable hole in my heart and head that I need to fill. I am desperate to know everything about this cancer I have. Only knowledge, I think, will get me through this crazy journey. But nothing brings comfort. Where is the information that says it will be easy, quick, and painless? Tears hover just below the surface and a large lump sticks in my throat. I realize that I'm frantically searching for every bit of hope that is out there. Who has survived? How did they survive? How can I do what they did?

When I finally look up at the clock on the wall it reads 10pm. I take a deep breath. I've been here for the last 6 hours, but I'm not tired. The adrenaline flows strong and steady. It's keeping me going. I know that if I let up, I'll collapse into a fetal ball, holed up under the covers and wishing this diagnosis away.

My head reels with this new language I must learn to speak: chemotherapy, radiation therapy, B cell, PET scans, neutropenic, staging, survival rates, sedimentation rates, prognosis. How did I get thrown into this steep learning curve of cancer? I feel as if I have been pushed off a cliff, my survival dependent on understanding my disease. One part of me feels the desire to push it away, screaming, "No!" The other part wants to do something, anything to ensure my chances of survival. If learning as much as I can is part of my dealing with this challenge, then I'll continue this upward slope of education.

This is one challenge I want to win. I want to live.

Initiation can feel like a rude awakening. As the shock and numbness that is The Call wear off, a sense of utter disorientation and sheer overwhelm can envelop you. It is as if you've woken up from a bad dream only to be living a nightmare. Everything is urgent and so much is unknown. As Shariann's story illustrates, this blend of urgency and ignorance can whip you into a state of adrenalized desperation, to do *anything so you don't feel so out-of-control*. Part of you naturally wants to return to a state of numbness, and another part knows you can't. You have entered the Land of Cancer and there is no turning back.

The learning curve at this stage of the journey is steep. This new land has its own vocabulary, much of which you are likely hearing for the first time. So please, have compassion for yourself. We can assure you, you will learn what you need to know in good time. This stage demands a lot from you, so treat yourself as you would a dear friend. Understand that this is all new and being impatient or judgmental with yourself is simply not helpful, not in the least. Having compassion for yourself will serve you now and for the rest of your journey, no matter what ensues.

Right now, imagine you're facing yourself, as if looking in the mirror. Tell that person (you) that you understand how hard things feel at the moment and, still, you'll get through this together. Because that's exactly how you will get through, by holding yourself precious and worthy. Now settle in somewhere comfortable and hug yourself close. Let's look at some of the questions that might be swirling around your brain right now:

- What protocols and treatment options do I need to learn about in order to decide what to do?

- How long do I have to make my choices? Am I behind in my treatment?

- Should I get a second opinion? Can I say "No," if I don't fully trust my doctors' recommendations?

- Would I benefit from alternative treatments? What other treatments are available? How would I pay for them?

- What about my *life*? Can I work? *Should* I work?

- Who should I tell and what will I say?

- What will my insurance cover? Will I lose my insurance if I leave my job?

If you don't know... take it slow.

The questions and possibilities seem so endless, you can stand amid them feeling paralyzed to choose. But remember, you don't need all the answers now. Just slowing down, prioritizing, checking in with yourself—all these can help you face the many decisions that confront you. In other words, if you don't know... take it slow.

Naturally everybody around you also has an opinion and has no trouble expressing it. Projecting their sense of alarm onto you, friends and family might push for you to "make a decision *now*." Or your doctor recommends surgery, your spouse wants you to get a second opinion, and your friend thinks you should go completely natural. It seems everyone must have their say—and, if you don't stay connected with yourself, it's easy to get lost in the noise and chaos. The Internet, as Shariann's story shows, doesn't help either. It simply adds to your fear and confusion, overwhelming you with information, much of which is unsubstantiated. For that reason, we recommend keeping Internet searches to a minimum.

Urgency and Agency—The Dance of Initiation

The first reaction to knowing you have cancer may be a powerful urge to rush into action. You have a serious and potentially deadly disease, and your doctors are already hinting that you may be "behind the eight ball." It's no wonder you want to hustle to make things better. But acting prematurely out of a state of panic, isn't going to help you make the empowered choices you need to find the best treatment path for *you*. As counterintuitive as this might sound, you have time to connect with yourself. More importantly, it's essential that you take that time. As with every stage on The Cancer Journey Roadmap, before you move forward, it's vital to understand where you are on the journey and how you are responding on the *inside*.

Yes, you have free will. You get to choose. In every moment.

We are here to remind you that there is much more fluidity and flexibility to this process than you realize. And you have much more choice than you think. For example, if you decide to go the western medicine route and you begin chemo, *you can change your mind*. If you want to start with a fully natural approach and you find that you want to switch to the western medical route, *you can*. If you want to take more time to get a second opinion, *you get to take that*. Yes, you have agency, free will. You get to choose. In every moment. This is where your power is.

For some of you, that will come as a relief. For others, it will feel like a burden. For still others, it may feel untrue. After all, if your financial circumstances and healthcare options are limited, doesn't that mean that you just have to make do and go along? Not really. While a wide array of options may not be available to you, you still have choices—especially those that involve your own attitude and how much you are willing to ask for and receive help, from loved ones and from your community. You have choices about asking questions of your doctor and not moving ahead with any protocol you don't understand or feel confident about.

The point is, you have more agency, more freedom of choice, than you might think. And once you've made one decision, it's not carved in stone. You can change your mind. Initially, one of our clients, Barbara, decided to take a non-western, completely natural, path to her healing. Months later, she chose to switch tracks to a western approach. Lots of people change their minds mid-stream.

There Is No Right Way

It is easy to fall into the trap of there is *one* "right way" to do this and if you don't do it correctly, you won't be restored to health. This belief is paralyzing. And it's just not true. So please hear this: there is no one right way. There is simply a way that feels right to you. Right for now. And that's enough. We sometimes call it the "real" way because it is authentic to you and who you are being, *in this moment.*

Like most people, your life is probably complicated and full of responsibilities. And the decisions you make about treatment have consequences, not just for you, but also for those around you. For example, do you have children? If so, will you need some extra hands to care for them while you seek treatment? Do you need to keep working to maintain a sense of normalcy or to pay the bills? Do you need to consider the logistics of getting to appointments, arranging for support, etc.? If you are worrying about your kids, or how to make your next doctor visit, you aren't helping anyone, least of all yourself. It's good to think ahead, to plan, and then move forward in a way that serves you best, *in this moment.*

The phrase, *in this moment* is key, because you will know more when you know more, and *you can change your mind.* Chaos and confusion are par for the course right now, but you can still trust yourself to take the next step, whether that's to begin a specific treatment, speak to a certain medical professional, have surgery, or just take a pause. Do what you know. Get the emotional and expert support you need and can access *in this moment,* and trust the rest will unfold. As Dr. Phil says, "It's about making your decisions right vs. making the right decisions." This is a helpful guideline.

Amy found an oncologist who said he could monitor her closely rather than do chemo right away. She chose to do chemo because she needed the peace of mind. "I knew I would be scared the whole time and have regrets later, if I didn't go with the chemo first."

Keri couldn't wrap her mind around chemotherapy. It wasn't until she spoke to an oncological naturopath who told her they could keep her healthy and manage the side effects that she could embrace a complementary approach.

On her fifth cancer journey, Shariann began oral chemo, and then stopped—even though her oncologist told her she'd get to live another day for every day she took the drug—because it was affecting her quality of life. On another occasion, she said no to a second stem cell transplant because she knew that her body could not handle that treatment, again.

You don't have to give your power away to "medical authorities" or other practitioners. It's helpful to slow down, gather the information, make lists of options, and see what resonates. Speak to those you trust to help you sort through your choices. Take the time you need to get clarity about what *feels* right.

We keep talking about not giving your power away, especially to the array of medical professionals who are now becoming part of your life. What does that mean? It means that if you have doubts, or if something doesn't feel right, or you want more information, you have every right to get your questions answered, whatever it takes. Let's pause a moment to look at what we mean by "power."

Power is the willingness and ability to act.

A definition of power we use is: "The willingness and ability to act." Sometimes we have the willingness but not the ability. Sometimes we have the ability but not the willingness. Gathering information is a great example because it requires both willingness and ability. It also reinforces the fact that you have choice, and you have options. You don't have to do anything just because an "authority" says so. It's your body and you get to ask as many questions as you need to, to get clear enough to move forward with confidence. (We have an exercise to help you get and stay in the present moment at the end of this chapter.)

One of the most personally challenging questions you face at this point of the journey is: To whom do you tell what? Maybe you've broken the news to family and close friends by now, but what about your other friends? And whom do you confide in at work? Maybe you've told your boss, but what about your colleagues? Your clients? Of equal concern, how do you break the news?

First, let us remind you, you don't have to tell anyone anything until you're good and ready—or at least until you can say the words out loud without crumbling. Kelly puts it this way: "Every time I told someone, it felt like I had to relive the news all over again. It was paralyzing. On top of that, I felt like I had to deal with their emotions about it, when I barely process my own."

There is no rule that says you have to tell anyone about your diagnosis. But here are some things to consider: First, how key is this person in your life? How helpful will it be for you to tell them? What support do you need from them? Do you want to put someone you love and trust in charge of telling people? Keri had a dear friend send emails to selected individuals to keep them updated. "It really took a weight off of my shoulders," she says.

The key is to put your own wellbeing first. Sometimes telling some-one close to you feels unimaginable at first, but they can often be the most helpful. For example, Molly felt she had to tell her boss right away because she was going to need time off for surgery and treatment. But she didn't want to tell her clients. So, she didn't—unless it felt right in that moment with that person. (We have an exercise to help you with who to tell and how to tell them at the end of this chapter.)

And when you do tell people, you may find that they respond differ-ently than you expected. Your closest work ally seems suddenly distant; your once reliable spouse falls apart; your jokey family suddenly loses their sense of humor; your closest friend has gone missing. What's happening?! You summon your Warrior self and say, "fine, who needs them?" But it doesn't work, because you do need them. And amid all that, there's the sweetness of having people come forward to support you. Maybe your spouse really steps up and is there for you. Your friends send loving messages of support. A colleague at work, who you haven't really been close to, sends flowers; a friend you haven't spoken to in years leaves you a voice message to let you know they're thinking of you. Your neighbor to whom you say nothing beyond hello brings you dinner. Your spouse's dad's girlfriend sends you a book. You get the idea. Having cancer can also bring out the best in people.

Setting Healthy Boundaries

While it's wonderful to receive people's well wishes, it's not always helpful to listen to their opinions or follow their advice. Even though they're usually well intended, they don't always know what's best for you, even if it comes from someone who's had your exact same cancer diagnosis. We realize setting limits can be challenging, especially at first. There's that voice in your head that says, "They're only trying to help," "I don't want to hurt anyone's feelings," "I feel rude," or "I don't want to make a fuss." Our clients often ask, "How do I set a boundary?" "How do I even know what boundary to set?" We want you to know, that setting healthy boundaries is powerful and self-loving. It is the voice that says, "This is my life and my journey, and I matter!"

Every cancer journey is unique. Claiming it as your own personal journey can be extremely powerful. One of the best ways to honor this is by setting boundaries. And while setting boundaries is important throughout your cancer journey, it is especially crucial at the Initiation Stage. Boundaries allow you to focus on your preferences and quiet the noise enough to hear to your own voice. They also stop you from worrying about what everyone else is saying. Boundaries are your personal limits—the lines you draw—that honor and allow you to be true to yourself. Boundaries make it safe to make your own decisions.

If ever there was a time for you to put yourself first, it's now, during a cancer journey.

But setting boundaries is challenging because most of us, especially those of the feminine persuasion, have never been taught how to set limits, or we've been discouraged from setting them because we could, God forbid, put someone off. This is a strong deterrent. Underlying the resistance to setting healthy boundaries is the fear that we will lose love and approval. In both our families (Shariann and Keri's) being called "selfish" was worse than a four-letter word. We were conditioned to believe that putting yourself first was just about the worst thing you could do. But we have learned different. So let us say this: *If ever there was a time for you to put yourself first, it's now, during a cancer journey.* (Side effect warning: Once you experience the benefits, there's a strong chance you're going to want to keep practicing it!)

You may be surrounded by loved ones who are waiting to love on you. And you may not. Regardless, it's important to be clear about what your limits are. We encourage you to ask yourself the following questions:

- What do I really want?
- What do I need?
- What is most loving to myself?
- What or who would give me peace in this moment?

(See the exercise at the end of the chapter for Setting Boundaries.)

Fear vs. Fear Stories

Keri's Story: I'm not a Statistic!!

"…Most people lose their hair after about two weeks," says my oncologist. Other side effects are … nausea and vomiting, bone weakness and pain, fatigue, numbness in extremities, loss of libido…"

My husband asks another question that I already know the answer to. I want to stand up and yell, "It's all SHIT, can't you see?" "Everything about chemotherapy sucks. There's nothing good about it! It seems like everything that comes out of the doctor's mouth is one more thing that will make me miserable. I want to strangle my husband. He keeps asking about the statistics. It's like I'm not even here. I want to run out of the room, and with the adrenaline I have, I feel like I could go for a very long time. "I am NOT A FUCKING STATISTIC!!" I want to scream.

I'm scared to death, and it feels like I have to face this alone, because nobody gets it. It's my body! It's MY LIFE I've already had surgery. They got "good margins" which means they got all the cancer. I don't have cancer. My body is well, healthy, strong. Why would I want to poison myself??!!

I can't eat because I don't know what to eat. Everything seems like poison to me. I have no appetite because so much adrenaline is coursing through my veins. I'm terrified. I have to DO something, come up with some kind of treatment plan. According to my western doctors, I can't start treatment fast enough. I barely have time to recover from surgery. I already have a date to begin chemo, but at this point, I don't know if I'll keep the appointment.

I feel like I'm racing against the clock and time is running out. If I don't figure out an alternative, I'm going to ruin my chances of being healthy for the rest of my life. They want to give me poison.

It's up to you, another friend says. That doesn't help me right now. I'm absolutely paralyzed. What if I make the wrong decision? What if I continue to feed the cancer, I don't know how I got here in the first place? I have to stop doing whatever I was doing that might have caused my cancer, and I would if I knew what that was.

If I get one more phone call recommending one more practitioner, healing retreat center, doctor for second opinion, supplement I should take, practice I should be doing, I'm going to LOSE IT! Everybody, just LEAVE ME ALONE!!! But please, Someone TELL ME WHAT TO DO!!!!

One of the biggest intruders into your cancer journey is fear, often paralyzing. Keri was terrified making the "wrong" decision would ruin her chances of ever being healthy again. She was frightened about diet, treatment options, just about everything, to the extent that she both wanted to be left alone and told what to do. Fear is like that—it reduces us to puddles of panic and agitation. Worse still, it steals our ability to make good choices.

So how do you deal with fear in a way that allows you to be sufficiently clear-headed to make the decisions you need to make? Again, you need to set a healthy boundary—this time with your fear. A boundary that lets you stay present enough to quiet the noise, to move through the paralysis, and step forward with confidence.

From where you are standing right now, we know this might sound like we've just told you to learn origami while flying to the moon. Most of us have a love-hate relationship with emotions to start with. We love the "good" ones and push away the "bad" ones. Fear and anxiety can feel pretty "bad," and if you don't deal with them, they tend to fester and get worse. In time, they can eat away at your confidence and ability to be present. But that leaves a puzzle: if fear is the go-to emotion of a cancer journey, how do you ever find peace of mind to cope with your situation? Here's the surprise: it's not really your fear that keeps you in paralysis; it's your fear *stories.*

Franklin D. Roosevelt famously said, *"The only thing we have to fear is fear itself."* We agree with FDR one hundred percent. You see, what makes fear so awful is not the actual feeling of fear. It is the Fear Stories—the stories we make up about our fear.

Fear stories are the scary stories that usually get bigger and more terrifying with each telling. When you create a fear story, your mind goes directly to what you are most afraid of, and soon you're busy making up worst-case scenarios. Anxiety follows, which creates more fear, which breeds more story, which creates more anxiety. The stories get worse and worse until we fall into a state of panic and paralysis. So how do we stop this cycle?

Fear stories aren't about what's real. They are made up stories of future scenarios that have not happened. They often start with the phrases, "what if …?" or "That means …!" What if I make the wrong decision? That means I'm going to die! What if I'm in pain forever? That "forever" word, like Keri saying that she might ruin her health for "the rest of her life," is a sure sign you are in a "fear story." And these too:

"That means nobody will want to be my friend!" "What if I lose my hair?" "… that means I will never be normal again!" "What if I can't trust my doctor?"

You get the idea.

Stories might begin with a question, and then your mind fills in the blanks with gory details. But one thing is for sure, your mind likes to make interpretations and stick to them. Like this one: *if* my friend doesn't call or come to visit *then it means* they don't care about me. Then you might add the zinger: "That means I am unloveable." Or that means they're no longer my friend." Then, you get incredibly mad at and hurt by your friend (emotions that you don't want to feel) and have to do something to distract you and to numb out. None of this has positive impact on your healing process.

Fear stories don't come from your heart; they originate in your mind, your wounded ego to be exact. Faced with an emotion you don't want to feel, like fear, your mind takes over and starts making up reasons (the story) of why you are or should be afraid. Remember that your brain is five times more likely to perceive threats than rewards. In fact, some have coined the term "awfulizing" for this type of storytelling: letting our imaginations run unchecked with horrible outcomes and explanations, absolutely none of which are known to be true.

Truly feeling your emotions in your heart is not the same thing as making up fear stories in your mind.

It bears repeating that feeling genuine fear (or any genuine emotion, for that matter) isn't nearly as awful as the anxiety and panic that is first triggered, then blown out of proportion by telling fear stories. And that, my friend, is an important distinction. Separating the fear and the fear story from each other allows you to explore and feel your actual and understandable fear, without escalating your anxiety or future-tripping awful scenarios. Simply being with your fear, minus the stories, unlocks the fear energy to move through you, shifting you out of paralysis. In fact, honestly feeling your fear is the only thing that will make it budge.

This is one of the most important distinctions we make on a cancer journey: Feeling difficult emotions in your heart is not the same thing as making up fear stories in your mind. One is powerful; the other sends you into panic.

> *Dottie sits quietly in a sunbeam by her window doing a crossword puzzle. Three across—four letters, "The name for a small body of water." "Pond or lake," she says to herself. Immediately the image of her summer home on the water flashes in front of her. On its heels, comes the fear of never again being able to swim in the lake. A dull headache grips her that persists for three days. Is the headache lingering too long? Is she having a recurrence or a metastasis of cancer that has gone to her brain? She is frozen with fear.*

Dottie is trapped in her fear story. The following story of John's illustrates how he broke free of his own fear story.

> *John is asleep in bed when a "bang" from outside his window startles him awake.*
>
> *It's the middle of the night, and his heart is pumping from the shock of the rude awakening. His mind starts to wander, "Hmm… my mouth feels dry. I should get up and get a glass of water. Why is my mouth dry? Is this a chemo side-effect?" He thinks, "Is the treatment even working? I've been so tired, and my body feels like it has been taken over by something I can't control. What if the cancer is spreading? I won't be able to go on the upcoming family trip to Yosemite. I'll disappoint the kids and they'll never forgive me. I won't be able to plan any future trips and they'll think I'm the worst dad in the world. How much time do I really have? Who am I kidding, I don't have any energy to do anything, forget about my bucket list. What if this is how it ends?" John's fear is clearly*

triggered. And then, because he is one of our clients, he remembered a three-step process.

First, he simply stops. He stops to notice the spinning stories in his mind, stories that were getting larger and more despairing by the minute. Second, he imagines he is listening to a podcast on the radio or on his device, and simply turns off the sound. When, after a few minutes of quiet breathing, he turns the sound back on, John gets curious. By getting curious, he becomes the observer of his thoughts and stories, instead of their victim. He notices the "awfulizing" as the story gets worse and worse, and he is almost amused by the details and creativity of the stories he is spinning.

Finally, John asks himself two key questions: "Do I know this to be true?" and "What do I know to be true in this moment?" The answer to the first question is, "No, I don't know this is true." The answer to the second question is, "I have a dry mouth." That's all he knows to be true. That, and the fact that he is making up stories and scaring the bejesus out of himself.

Once John takes himself through this process, he is freed up to choose how to respond. He decides to go back to sleep which, thankfully he can now do, and to call his doctor in the morning to ask about side effects.

As you can see in these examples, we can be triggered at any moment to feel fear and to create a fear story. Fear seems to have a mind and life of its own. And as John's story illustrates, the key is to stop and get present enough to notice that you are running a "fear story." Once you recognize that a fear story (the story in your mind) has begun, you can stop the snowballing and overwhelm of panic by becoming a curious observer, which then frees you up to take action, if needed. In John's case, he went back to sleep.

A Last Word about Initiation

We know this has been quite the chapter. It is, after all, quite a stage in your Cancer Journey. Don't worry if you didn't take everything in on the first go round. You can always read through it again, and the exercises that follow will help you integrate what we've been talking about.

But we do want to say this: You are braver and smarter than you can imagine. We've walked literally hundreds of men and women through the stage of Initiation, and at first they have felt as if they couldn't bear to take another step, another moment, of this kind of chaos and confusion and fear. So yes, it's like that—but it doesn't stay like that.

Remember:

- Hold yourself with compassion

- Take it slow until you know

- Realize that fear is one thing, your fear story is quite another

- You will learn and make the right decision, for you, in the moment.

- This is your journey, and you are learning to walk it in a way that serves you, every step of the way.

ADDITIONAL EXERCISES

Exercise: Getting into the Moment

To help you get present in the moment, we created a simple framework. It is called the P.E.S.H. Scale, which stands for P- Physical, E-Emotional, S-Spirit/Spiritual (Your own inner spirit or your connection to a Higher Entity), and H-Hope (Your outlook for the future.) To do the exercise, we have you assign a number (from 1–10, 1 being the lowest and 10 the highest) that describes you in each one of the P.E.S.H. areas, in this very moment. In order to answer honestly, you will need to get in touch with each of these parts of you. In that way, you'll not only connect with yourself, but you'll also have a snapshot of how resourced you are in each area.

Take yourself through the P.E.S.H categories, rating yourself on a scale of 1–10. If you need a bit more support, or you'd just like to check in with yourself even more consciously, we've provided the following guidelines:

Physical

1. Get into a comfortable position.
2. Starting with the top of your head, take yourself down through the major muscles of your body and tighten them for 5 seconds and then release. For example, tighten your scalp (count to 5), relax. Then, tighten your face (count to 5), relax. Next, tighten your neck (count to 5), relax. Tighten your shoulders (count to 5), relax… continue all the way down to your toes.
3. By the time you've done this all the way down to your toes, you are present and connected. In your body.

Emotional

1. With your relaxed, quiet body, take a moment to check-in with how you're feeling. Are you anxious, scared, mad, calm? Notice and name what you are feeling.
2. Now, tune into where that feeling is living in your body (again, anywhere but your mind). Feel the sensation of this emotion in that body part. What does it feel like? Is it buzzing, a knot, a ball? Getting in touch with what you are feeling and the sensation of it in your body will bring you more into this present moment.

Spirit/Spiritual

1. First, make the decision to connect with your inner Spirit (we also call this your inner flame) or with your Spirituality, whatever you call a higher power, be that God, Goddess, The Universe, Spirit, The Divine.

2. Whichever one you choose is generally felt from your heart. So, put your hand on your heart, close your eyes and allow yourself to feel your connection. Is your inner flame "Spirit" flickering or flaming (or anything in between)? Depending on how you imagine it, is your connection to your Spirituality a thin thread or a solid rod (or anything in between)? Notice how this feels in this moment.

Hope

1. After connecting to the Physical, Emotional and Spiritual parts of yourself in the above exercise, you should feel more present. From here, give yourself a number that reflects your level of Hope (your sense of knowing that all will be well no matter what) in this moment.

2. Using the same scale from 1–10, just notice and choose the number that feels right. It doesn't mean anything about you, other than your sense of Hope is high or low in this moment. Noticing will also bring you more into the present moment because it is honest and true, not something you *should* feel.

3. Being real with how much Hope you have in any given moment is freeing. It allows you to not have to perform for anyone, including yourself.

Again, the purpose of being "*in this moment*," is to bring you to the place where your power lives. You only have power in this very moment. So, once you are here, you can make decisions and choices that are true to yourself.

Your Guide: How to Tell Others About Your Cancer

How you share the news of your cancer diagnosis can affect how your news is received. If you can get clear first, you will minimize discomfort, for yourself and others. You can also make sharing about your cancer part of building a powerful support team. So, it makes sense to think about and choose whom you tell, and how and when you tell them.

You will have your own personal preferences, but here are some guidelines:

1. Gain Clarity. How, precisely, do you want to be supported during your cancer journey? Make a list in your journal of ways you want to be supported, the more specific the better. For example: Do you want people to bring you food? If so, what kind? Do you want phone calls, or do you prefer texts? Do you want flowers? Cards? Visits? It might be helpful if you have the luxury, to talk to a trusted family member, friend, or even Cancer Journey Coach about your needs.

2. Appoint Your Posse. Make a list of those who can help provide support (physical, mental, and spiritual). Who would be ideal to support you in what capacity? For example: Keri put a dear friend in charge of sending updates and requests to a select group of loved ones. That way, she could talk with one person and know she didn't have to repeat herself. You might want to separate your list into categories: Communication, food, family, friends, people at work, etc.

3. Journal what you want to say. Writing out what you want to say to each category of people will make it easier to have the conversation. For example, you may want to share more with family and close friends and less with the people at work. Share only what makes you feel comfortable and safe.

4. How to tell them. How to share news of your cancer depends on the level of intimacy you have with the people you are telling. For family, you might want to have an in-person or video call. For friends, it could be the same, or you could write an email (or have someone you love and trust do it for you.) And, for work colleagues (other than your HR person and boss), you might want to use email or a shared community forum like "Caring Bridge" which can be administered by you or a trusted beloved. Even if you don't want to share your diagnosis with many people, there will be individuals in your life who want and need to know.

5. When to tell them. Outside of your most intimate circle, timing is completely based on your needs. Most important is to first take the opportunity to process what is happening to you. After you have allowed your situation to sink in, you will have better clarity of mind and an easier flow of emotions with which to share your news with others. Helpful hint: Don't feel you have to do this alone. Don't be afraid to ask for help.

The bottom-line is that *you* are in charge when it comes to how to communicate your cancer diagnosis. How and when *you* want to and with who is your privilege and preference. As you will experience along your cancer journey, this is an opportunity to put yourself first.

Exercise: How to Set Boundaries

We often do not know one of our boundaries has been stepped on or over, until after it has happened and we feel upset, angry, or frustrated. Our emotions (our personal feedback system) let us know that something has just happened that we need to pay attention to.

Personal boundaries are guideposts that help you to feel safe as well as let you know you have what you need within you. This is helpful to maneuver in your life, but especially through a cancer journey. According to the book *Boundary Boss,* by Terri Cole, "Creating healthy boundaries protects you from emotional harm, keeps your personal dignity intact, and strengthens your relationships, including the one you have with yourself." We concur, especially with the last point. But short of reading another entire book right now, how do you determine what your boundaries are and how do you set them to make yourself feel safe? Here's an exercise that can help.

1. The first clue is that you're feeling an emotion, from annoyance and frustration to anger and rage. You feel you're being pushed or made to feel invisible. Hint: It's that feeling inside that makes you want to holler "Stop!"

2. When you sense this type of feeling, the next step is to take a pause, literally stop. Remove yourself from the situation and ask, "What's bothering me?" Is something not going as you planned or hoped? What happened? Did someone say or do something to you that triggered you? What did they do? Did they ask you something too personal? Are they giving you too much unsolicited advice? Did you forget to honor one of your values? What was it? Try to get some clarity around what caused the feeling.

3. Once you have the clarity, ask yourself the following questions:

- How did that boundary breach make me feel and how do I feel now? (Angry, enraged, embarrassed, pissy ...?)
- If you didn't have to worry about offending anyone, and could just say exactly what you mean, what request would you like to make of the person (yes, that could also be you) to feel like you're back in the driver's seat and safe? For example:
  - I'd like to take a break and recalibrate what I want since we seem to be hitting a roadblock;
  - Please do not talk to me like that, it hurts my feelings/heart;
  - Wow, I stepped on my own value of freedom and thought I had to do this in a specific way, let's see what way feels more aligned with my freedom value.

Notice how having clarity and making a request (even if it's just of yourself) shifts how you feel. Making the request is setting the boundary. Remember, it takes practice. And it gets easier over time.

CHAPTER FOUR
THE PIT STAGE

CONVENTIONAL WISDOM: I must keep it together at all cost. Otherwise, it means I'm weak and giving up, and I must never let people around me know how crummy I am really feeling.

CANCER JOURNEY INSTITUTE WISDOM: Giving yourself permission to feel intense emotions is key to getting out of The Pit and to becoming your powerful self.

"Vulnerability sounds like truth and feels like courage. These aren't always comfortable, but they are never weakness."
–BRENE BROWN

The Pit: A Dark Night of the Soul

The Pit is both the low point and the turning point in your Cancer Journey. In this section, we describe The Pit in all of its pain as well as all of its glory. We take you into The Map of Emotions and show you how recognizing and releasing authentic emotions provide you with renewed energy and a way out of The Pit. We give you opportunities to reflect on your own emotional state, and ways to explore specific feelings often considered taboo, especially for those with cancer. And we provide you with the key to release you out of The Pit and into the arms of your Allies.

Shariann's Story: Hitting the Bottom

"I'm stuck," I hear the voice inside my head say. And like lightning, my reflex to "push through" kicks in. "Click" it goes and away I roll. I'm poised in my running stance ready to ignite my laser focus and tap into my reserve tank. But instead of my usual sprint, like The Bionic Woman, I move in slow motion—click, click, clunk. Click, click, clunk. The "clunk" is the sound of my energy reserves hitting empty. "What is happening? This always works," I say to myself, incredulous at my inability to move any faster.

Deep inside I hear what I know to be true: the "pushing through" isn't going to work this time; it is wearing me down. Deeper still, my intuition tells me that it is exactly this habitual response of "pushing through" that has contributed to the cancer. I realize I have grasped onto my it-always-works default mode. And yet it is not working this time and I am unsure what to do instead. I have lived my life this way. Fear, sorrow, and loss begin to fill me. I curl up in my bed and hide out from the world.

For hours I lie there wishing I could disappear, when, what starts as a whisper, gets louder and louder, "Listen to your body."

The words keeps repeating, as if I have landed in some scary movie. I don't want to hear them and cover my ears in denial. "No, no, no, go away," I say inside my head, "I want it all to go away. You don't understand. I feel like my body has betrayed me. How can I trust or listen to it?" Silence.

There it is. The truth. I don't trust my body and now my power-through pattern is failing me. Where am I to go? What am I supposed to do? What is the answer?

I lie there for a long time in the silence and the fear. And then, in a moment of clarity, my heart says, "This is ridiculous, just listen," and I stop resisting. With a sigh that flows through me, for the first time in a very long time, I feel my body. It is tired. Not just, I need some sleep kind of tired, but bone chilling exhausted. It is like the energy and essence of me have drained away and there is nothing left to give. Nothing.

I have arrived at the emotional, physical, and spiritual depletion of The Pit. Tears well, hanging from my inner lids. Then, from deep in my belly, a tsunami of tears pours out. Every muscle in my body shakes as the release of the knowing comes to the surface. Hiding and denial are over; I am done with powering through.

The old way of dealing with my life, especially trauma and tragedy has worn out my body. I must find a new way. The tears release the grasp on my body, my spirit, and my mind. I fall onto the sofa, a rag doll, worn and beaten up.

Welcome to The Pit

We're not going to sugar coat it. The Pit is the low point on the Cancer Journey Roadmap. Named for what it is—dark, lonely, baffling—The Pit is where the painful feelings and physical depletion that are part of a cancer journey overwhelm you, dragging you at times into the depths of despair. But we can also tell you this: by allowing yourself to slide into The Pit you will open yourself up to face and feel your emotions in a process that can lead to profound healing.

Through our own personal experiences and having worked with hundreds of clients over the years, we have found that the only way out of difficult emotions is to go through them. We are going to follow that model here. We will take you into The Pit in order to get you through it. And *we will get you through it.*

With all of that said, it's important to realize that as cancer individuals, we follow the same roadmap, but every stage is uniquely experienced. Some Pit Stages are more intense than others. Some last longer than others. We believe that the deeper you are willing to go into The Pit, and the greater the darkness you experience, the more you create space for the light of transformation that is to follow. One of the most poignant lines from Kahlil Gibran's *The Profit* goes, "*The deeper that **sorrow** carves into your being, the more joy you can contain.*" But the sorrow, the pain, comes first. It carves the way.

Meanwhile, cancer hurts. It hurts in all kinds of ways. We are often acutely aware of the physical pain, but the emotional and mental pain cut even more deeply. What makes this kind of pain so hard to be with is that the hurt is invisible, isolating and without immediate relief. It is hardly surprising that we sometimes get nervous giggles in our workshops when Shariann says The Pit is her favorite part of the journey. But she's telling the truth.

The Pit really is Shariann's favorite. Why? Because it's the turning point of the journey. After the turmoil of Initiation, in the quiet that is The Pit, you encounter your emotions. And if you choose to honor them rather than ignore them, you will come through this journey with a deeper knowing of who you truly are. Instead of being emotionally and spiritually depleted, you will emerge with a sense of hope and wholeness. The Pit is where lasting transformation begins. So, let's look at what brought you here.

The Slippery Slide into The Pit

If we were to offer two words to describe the slide into The Pit they would be "emotional overwhelm." The mix of feelings you didn't have the time and space to process in Initiation, now swirl inside of you. This mix includes the feelings you most tend to avoid. They consist of, but are not limited to, disappointment, despair, fear, and anger.

In Initiation, a flurry of big decisions and agonizing choices about your treatment kept you distracted. Now that things are less frantic, deeper feelings begin to emerge. You may have encountered disappointments with treatments that didn't pan out as you hoped or made you feel sick and depressed. You may feel torn apart by a multitude of opinions and voices or completely exhausted by everything that is piling up—from dirty laundry to unpaid bills. It is all so very overwhelming. No surprise, then, that it brings up intense feelings. Feelings you would prefer to ignore or make disappear.

The trouble is, the more you try to push your feelings away, the more depressed and stuck you become. Trying to power through instead of feeling what's here only speeds the pace and intensity of the slide into The Pit. And we know because we've tried it too. But here's the thing: Before you can move forward to the next stage on The Cancer Journey Roadmap, you must first fully inhabit where you are. And where you are is in The Pit. So, let's look at what it's like to be here.

Inhabiting The Pit

Keri's Story: An Emotional Release

I can't get comfortable. Even though I'm tired, my body is restless from the steroid and anti-nausea meds. I want something, but I'll be damned if I can say what that is. I want someone to come and check on me but everybody in the house is busy doing their own thing, getting along with life.

I want a snack, but I don't want a snack. My body is … well, it's annoyed, by everything. I'm so irritated. And my tummy is so upset. It feels like something is burning inside of me. I used to count on being able to gulp large amounts of water, but now I can barely sip it. What's happening to me?

I need some nourishment. I get up off the sofa to make a smoothie. I make it to the kitchen, and something comes over me. I want to scream and cry. My insides want to come out and it's exhausting to keep them in. I open the freezer and slam it shut! I'm so angry!! I'm so lonely! Why won't anyone come and help me I need help and I hate asking for it. My worst fear is being a pain in the ass. But I so desperately want somebody to help me.

I open the cupboard and the next thing I know half the contents are out on the floor. A bag of lentils explodes. Bags of dried goods are scattered everywhere. I want to do it again, so I open another cupboard and out go the pots and pans. The noise is cathartic and now I'm sobbing out loud and cussing and hurling things about. I don't give a shit. I'm just so miserable. It feels good just to stop holding it in.

Footsteps on the stairs means my husband is finally coming to check on me. I just want him to hold me, but I won't let myself ask him to. I can't. That would just be way too needy. Somebody save me!

Entering The Pit, you may feel as Shariann did, exhausted and defeated, a limp rag doll. Or, like Keri, you may be filled with explosive rage and self-pity. You may even, dare we say it, feel hopelessness, something completely taboo in the established cancer world. It can also be eerily silent in The Pit as the bustle of Initiation dies down and you are left with your thoughts and feelings. Not unlike standing in the eye of a storm, every frightened, angry, doubtful, defeated, lonely emotion spins around, trapping you helpless in the middle. We call this feeling "The Swirl of the Pit." And at some point, it will find you.

The Swirl of The Pit

You want to move forward, make progress, and feel better. But how do you even know what that means when your world has been turned on its ear?

A big part of The Swirl is made up of all the unacknowledged emotions you brought with you from the Initiation Stage. Another part has to do with control, or rather feeling like you don't have any. You try even harder to hang on, get a grip, but it doesn't work. You are caught in The Swirl—and it feels scary and exhausting.

We can say with certainty that none of the many hundreds of clients who have shared their pain with us ever felt better when they tried to alter or suppress their feelings. Fighting for control only serves to exhaust you and dig you more deeply into The Pit and its swirliness. Or it can freeze your emotions in place until after your treatment journey when they come flowing out like a tidal wave, prolonging your time in The Pit. Either way, this is the vicious cycle of The Pit. You feel out of control, but the more you try to exert control, the deeper you seem to slide into the churning abyss.

The desire to control is a natural response to fear. We all do it. Or try to, rather. Here, in The Pit, the feelings that get stirred up feel particularly overwhelming because they combine and snowball with the feelings you didn't have a chance to feel when you were consumed with doctor appointments and medical decisions. Now they seem to hit all at once.

This is what some of our clients have said when they were in The Swirl of The Pit:

> *"My best friend hasn't called once. I've lost her. I feel so lonely and confused. Why has she abandoned me?"*

"My body has betrayed me. I feel old and unsexy and tired. I hate this cancer body! I thought I would be the model patient. What's happening to me? Who is this person?

"I have to cancel my trip to Greece. I've been planning and dreaming of this trip forever and it hurts so much to let go of this dream! It feels like I'm letting go of everything that brings me joy! Like my whole life is getting canceled, not just my trip!!!"

"I might as well give up. I feel like I'm a blob on the sofa and worthless. I can't even wash my own hair. I hate cancer. I hate me. I feel like all I am is a burden to everyone!"

This is the emotional storm that happens in The Pit. We promised you we would help you weather it. As it turns out, weathering the emotional storm is also one of the steps for getting out of The Pit. Perhaps you've heard the expression, "*The only way out is through?*" We alluded to it earlier. This is very true when it comes to emotions. So, it's helpful to befriend them. We're going to show you how.

Befriending Your Emotions

Emotions are energy, and energy doesn't disappear. It has to go somewhere. When you stop your emotions from releasing, you're holding energy in your body, energy that isn't meant to be held still. This not only takes tremendous effort, but it also causes dis-ease.

Imagine the energy it takes to keep a beach ball submerged in a swimming pool. It's exhausting because it's going against what the beach ball naturally wants to do. But once you allow the beach ball to naturally pop out of the water and float on the surface, the tension and exertion release. Similarly, when you unleash the energy of a suppressed emotion, it ultimately gives you more energy. Energy that can help you to heal. Freeing your emotional energy so it can move allows, you to feel less tense and more alive. Which is precisely why, we want you to learn to shift from blocking your emotions, to befriending them. Releasing unresolved emotions is a vital part of healing.

Emotions, after all, make us uniquely human. They are as much a part of us as flight is to a bird. They connect us to our inner world and to each other, and the part of us that is spiritual. We need to have our emotions to evolve, connect and stay mentally and physically healthy.

You may have heard the term, "Emotional Intelligence," or EQ. Our definition has three components: literacy, agility and impact.

- *Emotional literacy* means you acknowledge not only the fact that you have emotions, but also that you have a full range of emotions.

- *Emotional agility* means that in addition to the awareness that you have of your emotions, you can feel your feelings without judging them.

- *Emotional impact* means you take responsibility for the fact that having your feelings (and not having them) affects not only you, but also everyone you come in contact with.

Despite its tremendous importance and power, most of us have muddled through life never knowing how to develop our own EQ. Because Emotional Intelligence is so helpful on a cancer journey, we're going to help you increase yours. Starting with literacy.

The Map of Emotions

We created this map because we believe it shows a full range of feelings—everything from hopelessness and despair to love and freedom. It also represents the dynamic nature of emotions by taking the shape of a spiral.

Certain emotions like hopelessness and despair are found at the bottom tip of the spiral where the map is more constricted. Other emotions are at the top, where the spiral opens up or expands. We don't describe feelings as good or bad, but this map allows us to make the distinction that some feelings are more constricting and others more expansive.

All emotions are important. And we will say more about that in a bit. Meanwhile, you are gaining Emotional literacy by becoming familiar with the Map of Emotions. It will help you notice and name your feelings and to understand them in terms of where they are on the map and how you experience them in your body.

But EQ is so much more than learning the vocabulary, you're also going to develop a sense of the agility and fluidity of emotions, in essence, their dynamism. Ultimately, that means you'll be a lot less likely to get stuck in overwhelm, pain, or numbness, affectionately known as the tornado of The Pit.

Two important things to know about emotions are:

1. E-motions are "energy in motion," and
2. Each has a specific vibration, ranging from high, fast and expansive at the top of the spiral, to low, slow and constricting at the bottom.

The spiral represents how emotions feel in your body. Looking at the map, the feelings on the upper and wider, more open part of the spiral, vibrate at a higher frequency and feel more expansive and spacious in your body than the ones on the lower, more narrow and constricted part, that can make you feel physically pinched or restricted. When you experience the emotions located in the middle part of the map's spiral, you sense that you are either moving toward more expansion or more constriction, so we refer to those as "transitional."

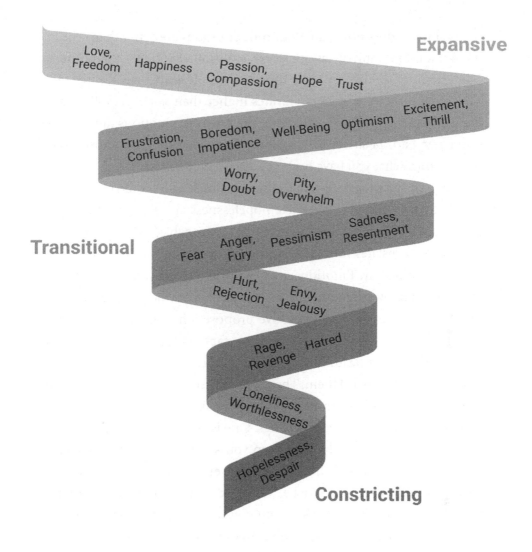

E-motions are "energy in motion,"
and each has a specific vibration, ranging
from high, fast and expansive; to low,
slow and constricting.

Again, this does not mean that some emotions are better than others. As you are undoubtedly aware, some emotions *feel* better than others. For example, feeling happy is much more pleasant than feeling sad. That's because *happy* energy vibrates higher than *sad* energy. But they are both energy. As we said before, the truth is, emotions are neither good nor bad, positive nor negative. They just are. This most likely differs from what you have been conditioned to believe.

Many cultures teach certain feelings are "bad" and should be avoided, especially the "extreme" ones like hopelessness and rage, or even happiness and passion. We are taught to be "reasonable," "in control," and that often translates into shutting down the energy of our emotions, which is unhealthy. Emotions are a natural part of you, and pushing them down or away ignores and discounts part of who you are and how emotions are designed to work. We propose a healthy alternative: accepting your emotions because they are a fact of life and honoring them because they are a beautiful part of your humanity. The way to honor your emotions is to feel them. They are your feedback system telling you that something is happening and wants your attention. There are two essential reasons to feel your feelings. One is, you don't want the energy to get stuck in your body or to keep you stuck in unhealthy behavior patterns. The other is, feeling allows your emotions to be the feedback mechanism they are meant to be. They give you feedback on everything you are experiencing: what's working and what isn't, what you enjoy and care about and what you don't. In other words, feelings allow you to engage in the art of living. By feeling, you are keeping that feedback system clean and clear and trustworthy.

We propose a healthy alternative: accepting your emotions because they are a fact of life and honoring them because they are a beautiful part of your humanity.

As energy in motion, emotions naturally want to move. Sometimes we think of them as static because we get stuck in one or another, but that is not their true nature. Emotions are dynamic, not static. As a human being, you can access the vibrations of every one of the emotions on this map, which means you have the capacity to feel them. (Note: this map illustrates a full range of emotions, but it does not contain every emotion." Feeling an emotion means allowing its energy to move through you, rather than it becoming stuck somewhere in your body. This, as you can imagine, becomes harmful over time because blocked energy adversely affects your health. Just like your blood and your breath, energy needs to flow.

Honoring your feelings is something only you can do, and it comes with lots of benefits. To genuinely feel your emotions, you must be in the present moment. That's where you access your power. It's only available to you when you're present. What's more, when you feel your feelings and don't try to divert your attention somewhere else or hold them tightly inside, you unleash the energy of that emotion, which ultimately gives you more energy, more life force.

Feeling your feelings returns you to your powerful self.

Let's Get More Intimately Acquainted With The Map of Emotions

Start at the lowest point, Hopelessness and Despair (they are not the same emotion, but do vibrate at the same level). The vibration gets higher as you move up the map until it reaches the highest resonating emotions, represented by Love and Freedom. Then, use your finger to help you, or simply imagine taking every turn and pausing on each emotion. Greet each feeling by naming it as you make your way through the spiral. See how much of each emotion you can allow yourself to feel.

Remain curious and simply notice your reactions. Are you able to feel a particular emotion easily? What goes through your mind? How do you experience it in your body? Notice each one. If you cannot find the emotion within yourself or just come up blank, make a note of that and move to the next one.

As you experience the expansive emotions, you'll notice that you physically feel more open, as if your arms want to spread wide. Because Love and Freedom vibrate at the highest frequency on the map, their expansiveness allows you to breathe fully. When you truly feel Love or Freedom, you literally feel "high." If you're moving upward on the map, you will physically feel your heart energy begin to expand. If you're moving downward on the map, you will feel more constriction. Stay curious and allow this exercise to be an exploration.

Love and Freedom are **not better than** Hopelessness and Despair. But they do **feel** different.

As you feel the feelings on the lower part of the spiral, you might notice your shoulders slumping or that it is hard to breathe. That's because hopelessness and despair vibrate at the lowest frequency, and your body tends to be more concaved and closed off when you experience them. Our clients tell us these emotions make them want to "curl up in a ball" or fetal position. You can easily see how emotions affect your body and why the emotions on the higher turns of the map feel better than the lower ones. Just remember, there is no hierarchy. Love and Freedom are *not better than* Hopelessness and Despair. But they do *feel* different.

Consider other types of frequencies we deal with every day—sound and light. We might *enjoy* higher notes to lower notes, or darker colors to lighter colors, but we don't say that high notes are *better than* low notes or that deeper hues are *good* and lighter ones are *bad*. We accept that they are just a range of frequencies. In fact, it would be pretty boring if all we had was one note or everything was the same color, right? The same is true for feelings. Even though we might think we prefer to feel the higher frequencies, like happiness and freedom, it's the range, variety and contrast that make life real and you whole-hearted. This is so important to remember on a cancer journey. Allowing the dynamism of your emotions unlocks energy that might otherwise get stuck. It also opens a natural process of healing.

> Allowing the dynamism of your emotions unlocks energy that might otherwise get stuck and opens a natural process of healing.

No matter what is happening to you on a physical level, it's important to know: Nothing brings you into the present moment and your personal power more potently than feeling your feelings. And nothing makes you feel more alive than when you are having an emotional experience, whatever it is.

Yet we close off our feelings all the time, especially on a cancer journey, because so many intense and difficult emotions are triggered. Not only that, we've been told to "*stay positive*" at all cost. And, let's face it, that's not exactly how we feel much of the time. Rather than allow ourselves to feel "*down in the dumps*," which is what we might *truly* feel, we shut our feelings off and go numb. We tell ourselves that to be socially accepted—and therefore to receive the love and support we crave—we need to put on a happy or brave face.

It turns out it's easy to shut your feelings down. The quickest way is to judge them, something most of us learned to do at a very young age. Imagine a child (or a grown-up for that matter) who is over-the-moon with delight until someone tells them to "*Calm down!*" Children naturally cry out loud with hurt and squeal loudly with joy and delight, until they feel criticized. *"Don't be a cry baby!" "Keep your voice down!"* *"Stop drawing attention to yourself."* Before long, we are conditioned to shut ourselves down—before anyone else can. A word of caution: please don't judge yourself for judging your emotions! Judgment is something you have to unlearn, so try to be patient, get curious and stay open.

At this point, you may be thinking, okay, I get that I need to honor my feelings. But how do I do it? Even though emotions are natural, but because we've become so good at pushing them away, we often need help accessing them. Mostly, that involves slowing down enough to notice. Here's a process for getting in touch with your feelings. While remaining open and curious, find a quiet space and allow yourself at least fifteen minutes of uninterrupted time, so you don't have to rush. Make sure your body is comfortable (or as comfortable as is possible in this moment).

Exercise: Feeling Your Feelings

1. Close your eyes, tune into your breath, and feel the energy vibration coursing through your body.

2. Look at the Map of Emotions and find the emotion that matches what you're sensing. Sometimes we notice more than one emotion drawing our attention. We suggest working with the one that has the most energy, in this moment.

3. Name the feeling. Say it out loud. As you say the emotion, notice where you feel the vibration the most in your body. Is it in your belly? Your shoulders? Your heart?

4. What are you experiencing about the vibration? Is it slow and dense? Frenetic and swirly? Or maybe, it's effervescent and light. To help you be with the emotion, you might imagine the color, temperature or texture of this energy.

5. As you sense it, allow the energy to flow through your body. You may have a reaction to the emotion: tears,

growling, cursing, and laughing. Allow that reaction to also flow.

(Note: We consider tears to be healing and we can tell you that if you start crying, it's important to let it happen. And you will stop. We promise.)

6. As you allow the flow of emotion, notice when and how it shifts. (This is good feedback because when you really feel the emotion, it always shifts).

7. Stop and notice. Sometimes, you get messages from your emotions. When this happens, it's helpful to make note of them and what they mean to you.

Allowing yourself to feel your emotions may feel alien at first, especially if you've lived a life of being taught and told to hold them in and "*be a good soldier,*" "*get a hold of yourself,*" and that "*showing your emotions is a sign of weakness.*" We understand. It takes practice. Truth be told, Shariann didn't really know how to feel her emotions and release them until she hired Keri as her first coach, in 1999. Today, she can see how her range and agility has expanded. Here's an example of what it was like for her during her cancer journey when she finally allowed herself to feel and release some rage.

Feeling your feelings allows you to be present, authentic and real.

Shariann's Story: Getting in Touch with Rage

I can feel a buzz in my body starting to grow from my belly, like electricity surging. I'm getting hot and need to take off my sweater even though it's a tepid 65 degrees in the house. I hear the words; "we don't have a prescription for your medication here" repeating in my mind, again and again. The body buzz is rising, and my hands are beginning to tremble. I want to scream, but my mind is still trying to make sense of all of this. "Didn't they say they were calling it in when I left the oncologist's office?" "Was I supposed to do something before they did that?" "Is this the right pharmacy?" I'm now questioning myself. I'm mad, but I don't want to alarm anyone in my household. But who am I mad at? The doctor's office? Myself? Both?

I've been mad for days now but haven't allowed myself to be angry. I've pushed it down and distracted myself. I'm afraid I will explode if I let it out. Then I remember, anger unexpressed becomes hurtful to my body (like a fart that is held in). So, I go into my bedroom and I close the door. "I'm safe in here and no one will hear me," I think to myself. I sit on the floor with my back against my bed. I take a deep breath, feeling my trembling hands, and the energy moving up my arms. Like jagged waves of red it moves up my neck to my face, which feels on fire. A scream wants to vomit out of my mouth. I grab my pillow and bury my face into it. "Aghhhhh!!! Aghhhhh!!! Arghhhhhh!!" the sound keeps coming out, free flowing. Then the words come: "I'm soooo f@#king tired of this s*&t!!!" "I don't want this Cancer…I want to be normal again…I want it to all go away!!!" Tears soak the pillow. The weight of this illness that was on my shoulders is now on the pillow. I let out a deep sigh. The jagged energy has subsided. I can breathe again.

A core idea: Your feelings matter. And so do you!

Being willing to have your feelings is an act of self-respect. Shariann was feeling anxious, agitated, angry and not present at all. But once she let herself feel her rage, she could breathe again. She felt returned to herself. Feeling your feelings allows you to be present, authentic and real. You are giving yourself permission to *be*. Authentically. Exactly as you are. As you take your cancer journey, along with becoming acquainted with the ins and outs and ups and downs of cancer, you are also being introduced to this core idea: your feelings matter. And so do you!

Being willing to have your feelings is an act of self-respect

It's okay if, unlike in Shariann's story, you're not yet able to give yourself full permission to feel. It takes practice. But once you get the hang of it, it becomes a habit. One that will serve you well as you travel the rest of your journey, with cancer or otherwise. Your ability to feel, to be authentic and to respond emotionally to your shifting circumstances will help you make powerful choices about your treatment and your life—choices that honor your truest self. What's more, navigating the next part of your journey will be eased with your newfound authenticity. The more you feel your emotions, the greater clarity you will have and the more powerful you will feel. It's not about doing it perfectly. It's just about continuing to try.

Here's what Catherine, one of our Cancer Journey Coaches, says about how this work with emotions has affected her. "*I felt emotions, but I didn't want to feel them. This [work] has helped me a lot to be healthy in my emotions. It's been transformative because now I'm much more present with my family, especially with my daughters. I feel so much freer because I'm being myself rather than trying to guess who I thought everyone else wanted me to be. It's like I've become so much more alive.*"

Yet, despite the obvious benefits, many of us are still afraid of our feelings.

The Reason We Are Afraid to Feel:
The Wounded Ego

The work of freezing emotions in place, rather than allowing the energy to move, is a strategy carried out by a very specific part of your psyche.

Are you familiar with terms like the inner critic, the saboteur, the committee, the gremlin, the judge, and monkey mind? These names are ways to describe the all-too-familiar voice that has nothing positive to say about you. The voice that compares you to others and usually has you come up short. Either that or it tells you that you are so far superior to everyone else you are barely part of the human race. We all have this voice within us. We refer to it as the wounded ego. It jacks us up, it pulls us down. And while its original purpose may have been to protect us, on a cancer journey, it causes untold strife.

Why is that? Because that inner protector part of you is unable to cope with what is happening to you. It is in panic mode. Your ego is in way over its head. So its wounded aspect is now on full alert. Thus, while you may always have had a fierce inner critic or a shrill saboteur, cancer acts on them like a steroid—they go full out.

Let us give you an example:

Astrid had been diagnosed with lung cancer when she came to us for coaching. She was grappling with spending money on an alternative treatment that would help strengthen her body while she was having chemotherapy treatments. She wanted desperately to make a decision and move on, but she was squarely on the fence. Whenever she seemed to be leaning toward one way or another, she would argue the opposite. It didn't take long to discover she didn't feel her life was worth the investment.

As with many of us, Astrid's first response to learning she had cancer was, "*What did I do wrong?*" While this is a very human initial response to a diagnosis, it isn't true, as we are mostly quick to acknowledge. But Astrid couldn't let it go. She listened to the stories that were forming in her mind about how she was being punished for that cigarette she sneaked behind the bleachers in high school. Logically, of course, this made no sense. A cigarette, decades ago, causing her cancer? It's almost silly to think about. But for Astrid, it wasn't silly at all. Her wounded ego had her in its grips and would no be quieted.

The guilt she felt greatly impacted her choices and decisions about treatment. Worse still, it undermined her means of coping and comforting herself. She was constantly dealing with the voice telling her, "*You got what you deserved.*" The more we delved beneath these words, the more we realized that the anger and rage she felt about her cancer diagnosis had been hijacked and turned inward by her wounded ego. This wounded part of her had supplanted her rage with blame: blame of herself. This dynamic is common, and it is one way our emotions get stuck. Worse still, it's not only unhelpful and unhealthy, it can be paralyzing.

> Instead of running away or trying to push it away, the way to deal with your wounded ego is to slow your thoughts down enough to recognize that it's speaking and notice what it's saying.

The point of telling Astrid's story is to introduce you to your wounded ego, and to empower you to see that believing what it says, is counterproductive. Instead of running away or trying to push it away, the way to deal with your wounded ego is to slow your thoughts down enough to recognize that it's speaking and notice what it's saying. Do you have fears and doubts that your wounded ego is telling you stories about? Is it scaring and threatening you with possible dire future circumstances? Or telling you, you aren't good enough or don't deserve to get the best care or lots of support? Write down or speak out loud exactly what it is saying. That will diffuse the intensity and allow you to see it more objectively.

Then ask yourself, "Is that true?"

Once you've identified the details of the story, then ask yourself, "*Is that true?*" This creates some more distance. Then you can *choose* whether to believe it or not. We hope you choose not to believe it, but just knowing you can choose helps return you to the present moment. Here you can feel your feelings and access your power, power your wounded ego no longer has.

Martina, one of our Cancer Journey Coaches, describes the gift of discovering her wounded ego, "*This work helped me become aware of my powerful wounded ego. I lived with it for so long, never knowing I could manage it!*"

Bottom line: your wounded ego doesn't have the capacity to understand emotions, so it responds to them as if they are monsters. "*Stay away from those scary feelings,*" it says. "*They're going to overwhelm you and smother you and you'll be consumed! Run, while you can!*" We've included the following exercise to help you understand and identify how this works.

Exercise: How To Recognize You're In Story So You Can Process Your True Emotions

We've explored how some very constricting emotions can show up during your cancer journey. Now, let's give you a practical tool to help you be with and increase your emotional agility.

Here's how we typically experience a constricting emotion and the story that keeps it in place.

(Note: The process is not always linear).

1. You're in a circumstance or situation that triggers an emotion experienced as a body sensation.

2. Your mind tells you—"*I'm under threat.*"

3. The mind (wounded ego) starts running a story—an interpretation—it says something like "*All is not well, I'm not safe, or I'm under attack…. That means …*" Then it begins to spin a story about a negative possibility in the future. The limbic brain gets triggered and you react with Fight, Flight, or Freeze. Left unchecked, the story continues and keeps you stuck, anxious and numb. Never truly feeling the constricting emotion, you continue to be caught up in the story. You think you are feeling the emotion, but all you are doing is playing out the fear story that's now on a loop in your mind.

What is true is that this pattern is following some well-worn grooves, so it usually happens automatically, in a split second, before we can be fully aware of what is taking place. The point is that we are "reacting" and not "responding" to the trigger. The reaction is a body sensation that sends us into "thinking mode" to make sense of the feeling in our body. Circumstance—Body reacts—Brain engages—Story begins. No feelings are felt, but they are right beneath the surface. You are so busy reacting, you don't know what is happening until you recognize that a story has begun, or you've already (re)acted.

The chart below can give you some examples of what this can look like:

(Note: We are working with emotions and situations that are typically felt in The Pit).

Circumstance/ Trigger	Body Reaction	Story/ Re-action	Avoided Emotions
A body ache that is present for more than a "normal/ reasonable" amount of time	Brain clicking searching for an answer, heart skipping a beat, nervousness in belly	*"Oh, no, the cancer has returned, is growing, is spreading in my body. I'm not doing the right thing(s). I don't know how to take care of myself."*	Fear Anxiety Worry Panic
Feeling exhausted with no strength	Fatigue, lethargy, lack of stamina, brain in fog or cannot function like before	*"I'm never going to be normal again and I am useless to this world." "I'm just a lump or blob and no one will love or need me."*	Hopelessness Despair Sadness Worthlessness
Best friend seems to have disappeared during your cancer journey.	Emptiness or hole inside, a disconnection from people, a feeling like you're floating along all by yourself	*"What happened to my dear friend? I thought she would be right here, by my side. Is she mad at me? Did I do something wrong? How dare she disappear in my time of need. I was wrong about calling her my best friend. Maybe I was wrong and I don't really have any 'real' friends. Nobody cares or loves me."*	Abandonment Hurt Sadness Disappointment Loneliness Anger Despair

Circumstance/ Trigger	Body Reaction	Story/ Re-action	Avoided Emotions
You're waiting for your appointment and the doctor is an hour late. Your medical center keeps sending you to different departments and no one has an answer. Or Your partner leaves you or your company lays you off (even though it's illegal) after you find out you have cancer.	Blood pressure rises and you can feel your face turning red. Your body shakes uncontrollably and your mind goes blank. You start screaming and don't even recognize your voice. Your heart is racing and your palms are sweating. Tears spring uncontrollably and your throat seems to close. Desire to punish others.	*"No one is seeing or understanding me. How do I get their attention? Am I invisible? Am I worthless I'll scream, shout, or do whatever I need to so that you can't ignore me. I'll show them! I'm not worthy. I'm just a worthless piece of crap.*	Anger Rage Hatred Blame Hurt Worthlessness Revenge Panic

Often, we cannot identify the emotion that is present until after we have been caught up in the story. So, when we realize that we are swirling in a story we can either pause or get present in the moment and check in with our body. With the help of the Map of Emotions and our body wisdom, we can figure out what emotion is present, so that it can be felt and processed. Once you've identified the emotion you're avoiding, use the process outlined earlier in the chapter to feel and release it.

Remember when you were little, afraid of the monster under the bed? Taking a running leap into bed to avoid the monster is a lot like running away from and trying to control your feelings. It doesn't make the monster go away. You might have made it safely into bed, but the monster still lurks and festers underneath. However, if you could muster up enough courage and curiosity to look under the bed, you'd see the monster in their true light. Not so scary after all.

Similarly, shining the light on your most "scary" feelings will bring them out of the darkness, and lets you see that your feelings aren't monsters, but simply powerful energies longing to be acknowledged and released. The bigger the emotion, the more power for you to claim. We're going to look at some "big" emotions that are common when you're on a cancer journey, namely: Loneliness, Hopelessness, Anger and Rage.

Spelunking In the Shadows: Loneliness, Hopelessness, Anger and Rage

When you go spelunking or exploring in deep dark places, you do it with the hope of finding treasures. And these "big" emotions carry the biggest treasures. We say this because they're the ones you most often suppress and that require the most amount of energy to keep down. Once you stop pushing them down, that energy gets returned to you as part of your power.

We are singling out these particular emotions because they are the ones we most tend to suppress and avoid. As we just saw with Astrid, the more intense the emotion, the more powerful and entrenched the desire to keep it at bay. Some of this comes from conditioning. But what makes it even more difficult is we can sense others' discomfort when we feel anything other than hopeful or upbeat. Everyone around us is terrified we might actually break down, have a hissy fit, scream, cry, fall into self-pity and rage. In fact, so much so that we get the subtle message that allowing ourselves to feel these emotions will make us sick. And, as you will recall, when we introduced you to Warrior in The Call, we also mentioned that we have this "battle cry" we are expected to take into our journey with cancer—armored and swords raised. But where does that leave us with these tender, painful, excruciating feelings that we need to feel?

Let us remind you that releasing the energy of unresolved emotions is key to your healing, and the price we pay by suppressing them is our own health and liberation, and that is far too big a price tag. So, let's put on our headlamps and go spelunking into the emotions that we tend to avoid the most. We have your hand and together we will find different ways to work with them so that you can receive the gifts that they hold for you.

Loneliness

"No one understands me." "My partner doesn't know what I want." "I feel so alone." "People are treating me weirdly." "Nobody gets it!" We hear these words all the time. Loneliness is one of the most common and intense feelings on a cancer journey. As you've seen from our personal stories and those of some of our clients, a cancer diagnosis can make you feel as if you are traveling a challenging road alone. No one understands what it's like to walk in your shoes and they certainly do not know what it's like to be in your body and mind. And it's lonely. This can be a trigger for your wounded ego to step in with some avoidance strategies. The first will be to create a reason, aka: a "fear story" to distract and deter you from feeling.

The rationale goes something like this: *"O my gosh, if you go there, you'll just be wallowing. And you'll stay there forever … which means you'll be lonely forever…"* Sound at all familiar? As seductive as it may sound to avoid feeling loneliness or any feeling for that matter, the truth is, it doesn't work. Ignoring your feelings doesn't make them go away.

So right now if you're sensing a feeling of loneliness, take a moment and close your eyes and just allow the feeling to come more present. Use the 7-step process for feeling that we outlined earlier in the chapter. Try to be with the physical sensation without judgment, without making up a fear story, and your feelings of loneliness will transform into a sense of peace and wellbeing. By embracing your loneliness, you reconnect with *you.*

After Keri had her cupboard-spilling fit, she collapsed in a puddle of tears and finally let herself feel the intense emotions she'd been avoiding. It was as if part of herself had been tugging on her, saying, "*See me! Feel me!!*" And when she finally did, the energies of loneliness and frustration moved through her and took her to peace and wellbeing, somewhere much higher on the Map of Emotions. The gift of allowing yourself to feel loneliness is coming back to the present moment with more energy and clarity than you had before. Ironically, feeling your loneliness is what makes you realize you are not alone.

Hopelessness

Hopelessness on a cancer journey? Are you kidding me? Aren't I supposed to stay positive? And there it is, the story that has you shun hopelessness. It sounds like this, "*If you let yourself feel hopeless, all hope will be gone forever.*" We equate hopelessness with giving up because that's what it sounds like when we let ourselves say what we feel. "*I don't care anymore, it's too hard.*" "*I don't believe I'm ever going to get better, (but I have to pretend for everyone else.*)" "*Chemo sucks. I can't do it anymore!*"

Michelle felt hopeless plenty of times on her cancer journeys, she just didn't know it. She needed Mark, her Cancer Journey Coach to help her recognize what was going on.

Coaching Interaction

It was a few minutes before Michelle's radiation therapy appointment, and she was being coached on the phone while sitting in her car.

Michelle: I don't see the point anymore.

CJC Mark: That sounds like hopelessness.

Michelle: No. I'm not hopeless, I always have hope.

CJC Mark: Yes, you do, but it just sounds like you're not feeling hopeful, right now. So, let's just be with what's here now. What does hopelessness feel like?

Michelle: Okay…it feels like I'm giving up.

CJC Mark: And what if you were?

Michelle: Then …I don't know.

CJC Mark: So, just make up that you know. What if you give up?

Michelle: I guess…that I would die.

CJC Mark: Yeah. So, what's true? Will you die if you feel hopelessness?

Michelle: No.

CJC Mark: Great. Take that in for a moment…take your fear story of dying and let it sit over here in your left-hand and be with the feeling of hopelessness, right now in your body. I'm here with you…

With the loving support and partnership of her Cancer Journey Coach, Michelle was able to get curious and honest about what she was feeling. She had a good cry once she allowed herself to feel the hopelessness. This cry was long overdue. A minute or two later, Mark checked in.

CJC Mark: What are you noticing now?

Michelle: I feel calmer.

CJC Mark: How's the hopelessness?

Michelle: Ummmm…it's not here.

CJC Mark: Okay. So, what is here?

Michelle: Calmness. I think I feel … like I can do this and it's gonna be okay.

CJC Mark: Good. I think you just reconnected with your hope!

When you have cancer, everyone seems to have an agenda for you to be and stay "hopeful." In other words, they want you to "*Stay positive, and never, ever lose hope!*" And this just feels like pressure. In fact, this attitude has a label, Toxic Positivity: the belief that no matter how dire or difficult a situation is, people should be positive. It's toxic because it isn't authentic, and it leaves you feeling like you did something wrong and will be rejected for how you truly feel, which absolutely isn't true.

The belief being put forward is that if you *feel hopelessness*, you've failed yourself and your loved ones and have succumbed to the boogeyman—the disease has won. So, you pretzel yourself and do everything you can in order *not* to go there. The truth is, just because you feel hopeless in any given moment doesn't mean that you've given up hope.

When you go spelunking into hopelessness (or any emotion for that matter,) you shift out of your mind and into your heart. And your heart will find its way back to Hope. Hope like the power of Dorothy's shoes, has been there all along.

Now, let's tackle anger and rage.

Anger and Rage

"*I'm so damn sick of this, I could scream!!*" "*Nothing is making me feel better!*" *My oncologist doesn't listen to me!*" "*Shut UP with the advice already!*" "*Don't tell me your 'ooga booga' cancer experiences!*" "*Leave me alone!*" "*Don't leave me!*" As cancer patients, if we are not saying these things aloud, most of us are thinking them. If you've said fed up, tired, frustrated, and just plain angry. What you may not realize is that these emotions, which we often diminish by calling them "frustration," are actually anger and rage. Recognizing these emotions for what they are and why they are occurring is extremely helpful.

Anger is what we feel when someone steps over one of our personal boundaries.

Anger and rage are like different versions of the same emotion. And they are very distinct. Anger sits in the middle of the Map of Emotions. Anger is what we feel when someone steps over one of our personal boundaries. Rage is in the bottom, constricting area. Rage is triggered when we feel invisible or powerless.

Rage is triggered when we feel invisible or powerless.

Women, especially, are discouraged from expressing anger and rage. But most of us, men and women alike, learn to keep these feelings stuffed down because we think they reflect badly on us. In other words, the story your wounded ego makes up is: "*If you feel anger, you're an angry person.*" You think, "*Okay, then forget about rage! That's where I draw the line! I'm not one of those people! I'm not violent!*"

Because we equate these emotions with violent acts, anger and rage are some of the most taboo emotions in our society. Why? Because we haven't witnessed them in their healthy expressions. The violent behavior we have experienced, and associate with these emotions, is actually the result of pushing anger and rage down. And like the beach ball we talked about earlier, the farther down it's been pushed, the bigger the eruption when it finally rises to the surface. Both Keri and Shariann vowed never to "be like that"—angry and rageful. They grew up in households where one of their parents, Shariann's dad and Keri's mom, had regular, very frightening fits of rage. So we understand as well as anybody the reluctance to go near these feelings.

But, if we remove the judgment for just a moment, we can see anger and rage for what they truly are: an inner alarm system that helps us know we've been disrespected or downright disregarded. The alarm system tells us it's time to feel these feelings.

Have you ever been so fed up you actually let your anger out? Our client Shelly remembers the experience of being upset with her oncologist's lack of communication.

> "*I had stuffed my anger for so long I was imploding and exhausted. When I finally let it out, I felt like I was thrumming with energy.*" *She got to feel it out loud with her Cancer Journey Coach as champion and witness and she was able to own the fact that she was*

angry, before she expressed it to the doctor. "I felt clear, centered and alive," she said, "I felt as though a burden had been lifted and I no longer had to pretend. It was liberating!"

This example clearly illustrates emotional agility. Shelly was having a power surge because she finally stopped pushing down her anger. Once she expressed it, it unleashed the fluidity and flexibility that had her move on the Map of Emotions from anger to well-being, and then all the way up to freedom. Not only that, but once she expressed her anger out loud with her Cancer Journey Coach, she was also able to have a clear, calm constructive conversation with her oncologist.

Setting Boundaries in The Pit

In Initiation, we talked about setting boundaries as helpful. Here, in The Pit, boundaries are absolutely essential. Remember, boundaries are limits that create safety. They protect us from being and feeling violated. Anger and Rage are built-in alarm systems. They tell us when boundaries are crossed and either need to be set or shored up.

> In The Pit, boundaries are absolutely essential. Boundaries are limits that create safety.

Let's start with anger. As we've said, anger is a signal that a boundary has been stepped on or over. One of the most common ways a boundary is crossed is when someone breaks a promise or an agreement. Let's say someone told you they're going to come over and they don't show up. Or your doctor says they'll call in a prescription and it never happens. Or, you've been told you should stay positive, when you're not feeling it.

When you look more closely, you can see how someone not showing up or following through; or telling you how you should feel; or even, making you feel dismissed, unimportant or slightly invisible, can trigger this feeling. It is as if they're broadcasting a message that you and your true feelings don't matter. Unfortunately, this happens a lot on a cancer journey. People tell you what you should do, how you should feel, and make promises they don't keep.

The natural, normal, *human* response to these situations is to get angry. If you are, that means your healthy alarm system is working and you can make a request to maintain your boundary. For example, you might say, "*Please do not talk to me that way it makes me feel dismissed.*"

Rage on the other hand is where we turn up the volume. Rage is when you feel invisible and powerless. Actually, we rage because we don't want to feel this way. Often this is caused by a boundary that is crossed, not once, not twice, but *over and over again.* This tends to happen when you don't set or acknowledge a firm boundary. Or it may be due to a person that habitually ignores your feelings. For example, an oncologist who continually dismisses your perspective will cause you to feel unseen and not heard, even like an object not a person. That's enraging. In this example, you might make a request that supports your boundary. For example, "*I feel like my viewpoint doesn't matter, I would appreciate it if you would hear what I have to say and take it into consideration.*" But not before you've had a chance to feel your rage.

Expressing Rage

If you're like most of us, you've tried to push your rage aside. And when you do, you walk around feeling irritable—it doesn't take much to set you off. Anything that smells the least bit like a dismissal is now completely intolerable and exhausting. The trouble is, it doesn't just go away with time, so ignoring or pretending it isn't there is not helpful. The rage you have kept from erupting seethes just beneath the surface, and you compound it by pushing it away. You're doing the very thing that caused your rage in the first place: dismissing yourself. So, what can you do?

Exercise: Rage Pillow

In our workshops, we do a "rage pillow" exercise, where everyone is given a pillow and, without much prompting, we all beat the floor (depending on your environment, a bed, a stuffed chair or other soft, indestructible object also work quite well) while feeling the fury of rage. When we stop the exercise, after about 15 seconds, everyone says they feel energized. We know that's because a bunch of trapped energy has been released. Do try this at home. Do *not* try this on another living being.

All you need to do to get the exercise started is think about how enraged you are at your cancer. But anything that really "gets your goat," really enrages you (e.g. your spouse, neighbor, the news, politics) will do the trick. If you're noticing that rage is hovering beneath the surface, set this book down and go do it now. Go ahead. We'll wait. ...

If you don't have the energy to beat the living crap out of a pillow, then close your eyes and *imagine* screaming at the top of your lungs, breaking a set of dishes, or destroying everything in your path. Let yourself be as destructive as you want—in your imagination. Another option is sitting in your car, not while driving, using it as a safe sound-proof booth and letting the screams loose. Keep expressing until you feel done. The release of the rage energy is liberating. And, we assure you this feeling won't last long. Feel free to repeat this exercise as needed.

Allowing yourself to feel your rage releases enormous stores of energy. If you let it out consciously and purposefully, your head clears, and your body is no longer encumbered by the need to hold it down. Now you can make the important decisions that need to be made. Now you have energy that can be used for healing—or anything else you desire. That's the gift of feeling your anger and rage. They not only carry clear messages, but they also contain huge stores of energy.

This is a great place to pause for a moment and review what we have covered so far:

- Lots of crazy intense emotions come up on a cancer journey, and trying to control them, (aka: avoid them), is part of what lands us in The Pit.

- The Pit is the low point of the journey, but it's also the turning point.

- When you let go of control and stop pushing them away, E-motions move through you instead of staying stuck in your body.

- When you stop controlling E-motions, you will feel grounded and clear, even uplifted and empowered.

Feeling and honoring all of your emotions, even and especially the tough or taboo ones, are extremely empowering.

This book is about you taking your power back and learning to live as your powerful, authentic self. Feeling and honoring all of your emotions, even and especially the tough or taboo ones, is extremely empowering. So, we suggest you take a moment to celebrate yourself for being willing to do this rewarding work before you move on to the last section of The Pit. It's something we hope you'll take with you into all aspects of your life and well beyond your cancer journey.

You are on your way, but you are not quite yet out of The Pit.

The Turning Point

Reading this, you could be in any number of places. You might feel energized by taking your power back with your emotions. Yay! But you could also be anywhere on the scale between that and feeling drained and overwhelmed.

You've done some amazing work, and we have some exciting news. Remember the feedback mechanism we spoke of when referring to your emotions? All throughout this chapter, you have been fine-tuning it. The tremendous work you did has created your very own personally tailored emotional compass. Now you are more attuned, not only to what upsets you, but also to what makes you happy. And we're going to use this information in the next section. This is precisely what's needed to get you out of The Pit, and why you are now at the Turning Point of your journey.

We want to acknowledge the fact that you digested a lot of information and experienced some deep-change practices, and while we believe it is all tremendously helpful, pace yourself. No matter how you're feeling, this would be a good time to practice self-compassion. Be gentle with yourself. Please take a break if that's what will serve you because we are going to move on to a crucial topic. It's called surrender. Surrendering is probably not what you think it is, but it gets you through the turning point on The Cancer Journey Roadmap. And, as we've said, it will ultimately lift you out of The Pit.

Surrendering What No Longer Serves You and Receiving What Does

Congratulations! You've done great work here in The Pit. You've faced and embraced your emotions, rather than push them away. And to do that, you've had to learn to put aside your judgments and be in the present moment. You've also found the will to set healthy boundaries. That is huge.

Because of the work you've done with emotions, you've cleared the way to see things you couldn't see before. With your shiny new compass, you are undoubtedly noticing things that are working and things that are not. These distinctions often become almost painfully clear. And, once the dust begins to settle, dreams and desires, including a longing to love your self that until now seemed almost dormant, will start bubbling to the surface. This is what it feels like to awaken.

There is one more courageous step to take—a step that will help to get you out of The Pit and set the rest of your journey in motion. That step is to set down what no longer serves you.

As we said before, allowing your authentic feelings led to a new clarity and calmness. No longer fighting yourself, you are learning to *be* with yourself. From here, more is being revealed. Specifically, you are beginning to recognize what, who, and how you are being weighed down. So take a moment to consider: What do you need to surrender or let go of? What no longer fits? Is it a pattern of behavior? A lifestyle, a job, a relationship? What feels like it's weighing or holding you down, or is no longer serving your greater good? What do you notice? Is there anything you can now clearly see that you might commit to surrendering, right now?

Shariann set down her life pattern of putting everyone's happiness and wellbeing ahead of her own, a decision that eventually led her to leave her corporate job in tech. Keri let go of not feeling good enough and became willing to ask for and receive help, a relationship game-changer. Alice realized the culture in her high-powered job in finance was eroding her spirit so she orchestrated her retirement. Susan surrendered a lucrative job in real estate and found a life calling to work with Cancer Individuals. Ann decided to not hold down her emotions and found the voice she had longed for.

We are not asking you to change everything all at once, but we are saying that if something in your life is no longer working, it will become painfully obvious, and with your newfound self-awareness, it will be more difficult to just sweep it under the rug or pretend something is okay when it isn't. You've come through a "Dark Night of The Soul," and with that comes a strong desire to be true to yourself.

Exercise: What Is It that No Longer Serves You?

We suggest you take some time, get quiet, and sit with or answer these questions:

- What am I carrying or tolerating that doesn't work for me anymore?

- What do I want?

- What do I *not* want?

- Who and what is holding me back?

As you contemplate the answers to these questions you may want to journal about them or discuss your answers with a trusted friend, someone who has no vested interest in your choice, but will stand as witness and champion. Again, we are not suggesting you to take any drastic action at this moment. Look at this as permission to explore, get clear and stand in your truth as never before. Allow the truth to guide you.

As you begin to let go of what no longer serves you, including the release of emotions you have held back, you will discover how freeing life can be. With this renewed sense of power and freedom, you will feel a lift in your mood, your outlook, and your connection to yourself. Lean forward, you are about to be welcomed into the arms of your Allies.

ADDITIONAL EXERCISES

Exercise: Rage Rant

Like a pot that's about to boil over, it is a good idea to catch rage before it spills over and out. Here is a mental and physical way to express your rage in a "clean" and "respectful" way.

1. Get out a blank piece of paper. Title it, "Rage Rant"
2. Set a timer for 10-minutes. Now free-write anything that comes to mind about your rage or what your rage has to say. You have the page front and back to express it (and more if required!)

Here are some prompts: What is enraging you? Is it a friend? A loved one? The fact that you've had cancer? A disappointment in your treatment? Your doctor's attitude or lack of listening?

3. You may have a string of words like *See me! You're a loser! F**k you! This is stupid! I'm so angry! I am not a loser, a**hole!* You may want to draw or scribble what comes up. What does your rage look like? What does it want to do? Whatever comes to mind, put it down on the page. Remember: No Judgment!

4. Once you have had your "mind-purge," rip the page up (Yes! you can). Just tear it to shreds with your hands. Feel your rage flow through and into the paper. As you do this, yell what you really want to say but never would. Let yourself go.

5. When you're done with the shredding, throw it in the garbage, take a match to it (in a safe container), or even flush it down the toilet.

6. Now, breathe and feel into your body.

Notice the energy flowing through you. It's amazing how much useful vibrating energy rage has and why holding it in and down causes such discomfort or "dis-ease" in your body. Any and all of these processing options can help you release your rage in a clean and healthy way.

Exercise: Getting out of the Mind/Story Swirl

1. Take 3 deep breaths to slow yourself, the mind/story swirl, and your body sensation down.

2. Notice the words that are swirling in your head and capture them by writing them down, talking it out with a Cancer Journey Coach or trusted friend, or record yourself. Do whatever is needed to let them out of you so that you can hear what your mind is telling you.

3. With the story out of you, close your eyes and notice the feeling in your body. What are the sensations? Now, with the Map of Emotions, notice which emotion is present.

4. Allow yourself to find where this emotion lives in your body and get connected with it. What does it look like? Shape, Color, Texture. Stay here, your body wants you to see and feel it. What sound does it make? A groan, a cry, a scream. It doesn't need to make sense, just let it out. It's a part of you that wants to be known. If you're willing, see if it has a smell or taste. The more you can get in touch with the emotion with your five senses, the less grip it will have. Experience it and let it flow.

5. Now that you're clear on the story, find out what's true. Ask yourself "What is true in this moment?" Listen and capture the answers.

6. Notice that the story has quieted, and your body sensation(s) may have changed. What are you feeling now? Check with the Map of Emotions again. Where are you now? Emotions shift naturally when they are truly felt.

Being able to separate the story from the emotion brings you back in the driver's seat. You are not a captive to either of these. You can see clearly and feel cleanly. This is you in your power.

CHAPTER FIVE
THE ALLIES STAGE

CONVENTIONAL WISDOM: Allies are people who come to your rescue.

CANCER JOURNEY INSTITUTE WISDOM: Your greatest ally is you. When you embrace that truth, the world becomes your Ally.

"Allies are the things that nourish and awaken our true selves. They lift us and assure us that we are not alone."
–SHARIANN TOM

Allies: Opening Up to Receive Love and Support

You are about to discover a whole new relationship to yourself, your friends, family, and world about you. Allies are everywhere! In this chapter, we show you how to recognize them and, most importantly, how to open your heart to receive their gifts of love and support. We take you through a process that includes grieving and self-forgiveness, to open you to a life founded on gratitude and the values you hold dear. The greatest of the lessons that follow: You are your best ally.

Shariann's Story: I'm Not Done Yet!

I look around to see what might make me feel better. For days on end, it was my lounge chair and the friendly drone of HGTV and the Food Channel. But today, I need something else; I need something that will lift me from my malaise. I don't feel like walking, especially since the hill outside my door is more than my tired body can handle.

My tired limbs rise from the chair and step out onto the deck. I can feel the sunshine on my face and a cool breeze. I take in a deep breath. Yes! Fresh air fills my lungs, not the stale air of inside. I sit on a deck chair and look up at the sky. It's blue with streaks of wispy clouds. The expanse of greenery on the hill behind my house soothes my eyes. I'm breathing better and my spirit calms. I watch the trees sway with the wind and notice their resiliency.

Tears well up and sadness fills my heart. How short life is. I let the tears flow. I am both sad to be so close to my mortality and grateful that I have this wonderful life. I can feel the life force inside of me insisting, "I'm not done yet! I still have so many people to get to know and touch and love. I want to stay. I want more of my wonderful life." I let the tears flow because the release feels good. I don't have to hold them in, fearing that I will make someone uncomfortable. In this moment, my flickering inner flame ignites and grows. I'm claiming that I want to live to no one but myself, and that is all that matters.

Welcome to Allies.

Allies is the stage on the roadmap where you discover the love and support needed to strengthen the connection to your new self. It is here that you begin to realize that help is all around you—and within you too. And we're going to show you how to access all of it—every last, delicious drop.

Imagine if you looked around and everywhere saw people who loved and supported you. Imagine seeing, truly seeing, the beauty of a tree or a sunset. Imagine if you had a deep sense of comfort within yourself—a feeling of self-forgiveness and compassion. Imagine if the tears of your grief served not only to release any lingering pain, but also to nourish what is already blooming in your heart and in your life. This is the promise of Allies.

So, who and what are Allies? Allies are the neighbor down the street who brings you soup, the friend who accompanies you to infusion appointments, and the practitioner who always has a kind word. Above all, an Ally is someone who doesn't impose their agenda on you, but who supports you in satisfying your own wants and needs. Allies are angels. They lift our spirits and take some of the burden off our shoulders. And, as you can see from Shariann's story, they aren't only people. Allies come in all shapes, sizes and situations: the music that calms you; the passage from a book that appears at exactly at the right moment; the scenery that makes you remember the world is still beautiful; even the cheesy television commercial that helps you cry when you need it most.

You did a lot of work to get to this point of your journey. You've reclaimed so much life force by befriending your emotions, and you even went spelunking to discover some of the most painful or "taboo" ones.

This cleared your vision to be able to see and surrender what no longer serves you. You have taken a huge step forward into the new person and new life that is awaiting you. And now you are about to discover a new relationship with yourself, your friends, family, and the world around you. As you step into your full authentic self and a life beyond your previous imaginings, you will experience a process with love at its core. It happens naturally and is often experienced as a softening and expanding of your heart. We have heard clients describe it in these ways:

"I think I'm becoming a mush ball!"

"I could never have said this before, but now I'm so heart-centered."

"I ask for help all the time, now."

"I feel like I'm learning what it means to truly love myself."

"I no longer berate myself when I make a mistake."

"I don't get as caught up in the small stuff anymore."

"I am a more open-hearted, collaborative, grounded, resourced provider, companion and person."

Yet, even with this promise and having done all of this work, you still might feel unsteady, or even sad. While all the changes you are going through are positive, you've given up a lot to make them. You are not who you were, and you have yet to become your new and transformed self. It is here that you begin to realize that help is all around you—and within you too. And we're going to show you how to access all of it—as we said, every last, delicious drop.

The Pit opened your whole being to the full gamut of emotions. In the process it connected you to your heart. Because of this, you are now more attuned to the people and things that feel supportive and loving. Not only can you now better see your Allies, you are also gradually learning to open your heart to *receive* all the love and support they can offer you. And it begins, as heart openings often do, with shedding some tears.

Yes, there is more to feel. You have already embraced the notion that feelings are your Allies and your guides. Now we are going to take you through a life-affirming process that includes the depth of your gratitude and the blessings of self-compassion and forgiveness. But it begins with grieving all that you have let go of. And, as we've said, you have let go of a great deal.

Grieving Who You Were

It may seem odd to think of grief as an Ally, but until you mourn the passing of what was, you will likely struggle to move into the new and next stage of your journey. The reason we include it here, following The Pit, is because we believe that you cannot access grief, until you have first opened yourself to feeling your rage, loneliness, and despair. Grief demands you first go into the dark, before you are positioned to experience it as the gentle, deep and cleansing process it is.

Grief is the acknowledgement of loss, but it also signals the awakening of our hearts. Through grief, you experience what the book of Alcoholics Anonymous calls, "The Sunlight of the Spirit," the lightness of being that occurs after completing the hardest work you'll ever do, and you are set free.

Cancer has stolen your innocence. You have lost the naïve belief that nothing as devastating as a diagnosis of cancer could ever enter your life, and that you'll live forever. Old hopes and dreams have been dashed. What was will never be quite the same again. This, we have learned, is not a bad thing. In fact, it sets the stage for true transformation. But before you can feel the deep joy of that—the wisdom of that—you need to let yourself grieve. Grief melts away your last layers of resistance to letting go of the old story, the old life. It opens you up to rest fully in the arms of your Allies.

Before you can fully rest in the arms of your Allies, you must take an important step and allow yourself to grieve.

Shariann's Story: Giving Up Who I Once Was

"I prided myself in being self-sufficient and the one who took care of things. So, when I was diagnosed with Cancer, I was determined to shield and take care of everyone while I tried to take care of myself. I'd done this before in so many different scenarios, caring for the babies, household, and husband, while holding down a more than full-time job.

However, I didn't have the reserves I used to. Cancer depleted me. I needed help, but I wasn't familiar with how to ask for and receive it. Wonderful friends and family would offer, and I kept saying 'I'm fine. I've got it.' This did not serve anyone. Most of all, it sent me into Martyrdom—equal parts self-pity and self-importance—and I felt so alone.

Even though the demand of this way of life was killing me, it was hard to give up the person I once was.

Shariann's example describes both the grief of leaving your old self behind as well as what happens when you begin to see clearly the patterns that no longer work. Grieving the fact that she would no longer be seen, by herself especially, as the one who took care of everything, was hard. She had to let go of being the one with all the answers. And that hurt. It can be challenging to grieve for how things were—how you were—both before and during your cancer journey.

Our clients have felt this, too.

- Diane had to grieve the passionate relationship she used to enjoy with her husband. After treatment, her body and her libido were not what they once were.

- Before his cancer, Samson was always a positive person and now had to grieve the letting go of his innocent belief that he was "healthy as a horse."

- Lillian grieved the beautiful symmetry her body used to have and the confidence that came with it.

- Marcus missed having the stamina and passion he once had to be able to work long hours for days on end.

- Jill grieved her relationship with her best friend who seemed to disappear once she began treatment.

You may also grieve things like who you were that you took pride in, who you felt safe being or what you loved doing. You might need to grieve the time you wasted by staying stuck in old patterns, jobs, or relationships, even after they no longer made you happy.

Allowing your grief to flow is vital. And it's a process, one you honor by taking the time to consciously feel so you can release and say good-bye. Below, you'll find an exercise to help you experience and release your grief. But for now, simply take a moment to reflect: What do you mourn? It's not only okay to name what you are grieving; but it is also vital to do so. And naming it can often be all it takes to let it go. For example, Shariann missed not being the one who everyone could rely on. And Keri missed the healthy, vital-feeling body that gulping water represented to her.

By allowing yourself to grieve, you release the weight of "what might have been" and move forward into what's next. Sometimes it takes a bit more to let something go, though. Sometimes it requires forgiveness—one of the most powerful Allies you will encounter on this journey. Forgiveness allows you to complete the grieving process.

The Power of Self-Forgiveness

Forgiving yourself is an essential Ally on your healing journey. It liberates you from blame and shame. It changes you. It frees you by opening the door to more love. And nestled in the space of love, all the stories about what you did wrong (blame) or how you *were* wrong (shame) no longer hold energy.

Forgiveness unlocks your heart with the keys of compassion and understanding.

Cancer has given you the opportunity to slow down and look more closely at your life, to make new, more powerful choices. These new choices won't "stick" unless you can let go of your binding past. Forgiveness, like grief, can be part of that release. It unlocks your heart with the keys of compassion and understanding. Where before you may have muscled and struggled to change or let go, now you are immersed in a warm river of love and forgiveness that gently allows whatever wants and needs to change. But to truly forgive yourself, you must first have self-compassion. In this next exercise, we are going to help you find it.

Exercise: Finding Self-Compassion

Once again, if you're not already there, find a comfortable space where you won't be interrupted for the next few minutes.

1. Imagine for a moment stepping into a judgment-free zone. Perhaps it's a beautiful place in nature where you feel very safe. Notice how relaxed and peaceful you feel here. Your critical mind has no power here in this calm, lovely sweetness.

2. Remember the state of mind you were in when cancer entered your life. Can you see your past self? How were you

feeling? What were you thinking? Were you frightened? Overwhelmed? Be with yourself as you would someone who you love deeply (i.e.: your best friend, significant other, or child). Find that feeling in your heart.

3. As you look at your past self, bring the understanding that they were coping the best they could in that moment. Sense how much you care about them. Notice what happens.

4. Let your heart open to feel the sweet sadness and tenderness. This is your compassion. Allow it to become a gentle, warm mist that embraces both your past and present selves. Extend your love and understanding to include your actions in the past with the resources you had then and all your choices that may not have turned out, as you wanted.

This is what it's like to become your own best Ally: to treat yourself so lovingly and gently. Sometimes, especially in hindsight, it's a struggle to suspend harsh judgment. We think we should have known better. But really, should we? Compassion tells us otherwise. Compassion is about having empathy and understanding for your self. And this is why compassion is a prerequisite to self-forgiveness.

Once you can find and feel compassion, forgiveness flows easily. So, if you are willing, take this exercise one step further.

Exercise: Forgiving Yourself and Taking Your Power Back

(Optional: Before you begin the forgiveness part of the exercise, you may find it helpful to make a list of the specific things you are forgiving yourself for. Begin the list by writing at the top of the page: "I forgive myself for …." Things like: yelling at my spouse, working so hard that I neglected myself, smoking 3 packs a day, not speaking my truth…)

1.   Begin by putting your hand on your heart to connect with your self-compassion.

2.   Say out loud, "*I forgive myself.*" Let that sink in for a moment, take a breath and say it again, "*I forgive myself.*" Once that's sunk in, say it one more time.

3.   Pause for a moment and notice your energy. What are you feeling? Relief? More space? More breathing room? Sadness? Happiness? All are appropriate and welcome.

4.   Next, it's time to take back the power you gave to punishing or blaming yourself. Say, "*I take my power back.*"

5.   Take another pause, and just notice. Notice the energy in your body, the thoughts going through your mind, the feelings in your heart.

6.   Allow yourself to feel your power—the power you gave away to the situation, act, or behavior—returning it to you.

7.   If you have made a list, now is the time to tear it up and/ or burn it. And as you do, say, "*I forgive myself.*"

8.   As a final step to this exercise, ask yourself, "*What's possible from here?*" Allow images, energy, and answers to bubble to the surface. Feel free to jot down notes, or simply let whatever comes to wash over you.

Forgiveness is one of the most powerful acts we take as human beings. Why? Because we are sending ourselves the message that we are no longer going to berate and judge ourselves, that as human beings, we accept the fact that we are not perfect, and that no matter what, we are worthy of love. Self-forgiveness allows us to re-direct and re-claim our attention, energy, and focus. And all it requires is your willingness. Compassion will come if you're willing. Don't worry if you're not feeling totally "liberated" this very moment. Sometimes forgiveness comes in layers. Sometimes it takes a while to sink in. Know that you forgave yourself enough, for now.

Self-forgiveness truly and fully releases what no longer serves you, and restores you back to your presence, to who you truly are. This is a giant step toward not only becoming, but also being your own best Ally.

Knowing you Matter

Forgiving yourself is saying, "I'm *worth* forgiving. I'm *worthy* of love." In other words, "I *matter*." Yes, you do. You always have, but forgiveness allows you to feel it in your heart. And this plays out in some surprising and extraordinary ways.

> Knowing you matter not only opens your heart, it also opens your eyes to the love and caring that is everywhere.

Knowing you matter not only opens your heart, it also opens your eyes to the love and caring that is everywhere. Through this new lens of Allies, you come to realize the world is not against you. In fact, the world is for you. And Allies are everywhere!

As you welcome in all of the many Allies to support you, you open yourself up to receiving more and more love and healing. You are expanding your world and your life. You can trust and accept yourself. And, as you do, you realize that you know what you need.

> You are truly your own **best Ally**!

Gratitude as a Way of Life

Let's take this a step further. Remember the Sunlight of Spirit we spoke of earlier? Once you have been brave enough to grieve what you have set down, felt self-compassion and forgiven yourself, you settle into the fact that *you* are your *best* Ally. You have learned to treat yourself kindly and with respect and it is extraordinary how this sense of gratitude for yourself grows to take in everything and everyone else. This brings you an amazing sense of lightness, even joy. The truth is, the more you love yourself, the more love you will feel and see everywhere around you. And the more grateful you will feel.

Now you can relax into all the loveliness that surrounds and encircles you: the warmth of the sun, the aroma of sweet jasmine, the taste of sun-kissed strawberries, and the caw of the neighborly crow. Now you can take in all the beauty that life has to offer. The beauty that is here and that has always been here. Seeing the loveliness around you, you naturally begin to embody gratitude. Not just in little moments, but as a way of life.

Gratitude is more than just being thankful. Love, joy, understanding and compassion are all part of the mix. Most powerful is the sense that you are not separate from anything or anyone. You belong—connected not just to the world about you, but also to yourself—your deepest authentic self.

Amy, one of our Cancer Journey Coaches describes it this way: "*I feel like I've reclaimed myself… I'm giving me permission to lean into myself, into what I bring to the world, and to trust it. I am beyond grateful.*"

As you continue to embrace yourself as your own best Ally, you begin to experience your depth, magnificence and capacity for self-trust. And maybe, just maybe things can come to you without you needing to earn them. Gratitude is something that expands and deepens the more it is practiced. It has the capacity to carry you through the rest of your cancer journey and beyond. And being grateful for your beautiful self is a lovely place to begin.

Let's take a pause here to reflect before moving on, maybe even make a list. What you are grateful for in your life right now. What are you grateful for in yourself? Looking through this new lens, what can you now see and appreciate?

Now that you've completed this re-claiming process, we want to give you one more tool that will help you and guide you through the rest of your journey.

Discovering Your Personal Values: A Powerful Ally

We hope that at this point you are sensing the healing momentum of all the work you have done. By befriending and feeling your emotions and having the courage to grieve what's lost over the course of your journey, you have created a greater awareness of your inner landscape, an amazing feedback loop. And with the tools of self-compassion and forgiveness, you have a means of righting and returning to yourself when you're been blown off course. This naturally leads to gratitude which blooms and blossoms in your heart. As a result, you now have both the ability and willingness to nurture and love yourself. That is the very definition of power.

As you settle into the changes that are taking place within you and in your life, you learn to sustain your courage and lean into your Allies to make new choices that are first and foremost in your best interest. To help you with this process, we want to introduce you to another of the most helpful and powerful Allies you possess: your personal values.

We mentioned values in the Innocence chapter, so you may remember that they are the principles you hold most dear, like Spirituality, Family or Adventure. Because your values are the essence of what's most important to you, they can serve as a guiding light or inner compass. Knowing them and honoring them daily are part of what will allow you to live a life of purpose, meaning and happiness going forward.

Since being in The Pit, you may notice that your values and priorities have shifted, been jostled, or completely dissolved. That's part of your transformation. Your true values guide you to live your own beautiful life, rather than someone else's.

We see this in Marjorie's story:

> *Life before cancer was focused on work. I was the first one through the door in the morning and the last one to turn-off the lights. When a client needed something, I was there, day or night. It was as if the company coursed through my veins. Then, cancer knocked me down. I felt as if I was put through a washing*

machine—everything was flipped inside, out. When I pulled myself right side up, I could see that I was living for the constant approval and recognition of my boss and clients. It was a sad realization, but it also gave me a chance to see what was truly important. I missed my children growing up because of work and I didn't want to miss it with grandchildren. I wanted to be the grandma who shared sage wisdom, belly-hurting laughter, and safe, cozy love. I wanted to matter in their lives. And I needed to own that I had a purpose other than work. Cancer showed me how I wanted to matter to my family, and I needed to take care of myself so that I could also make a difference in their lives.

Marjorie's values shifted during her cancer journey. She went from prioritizing "Work" at the top of her list to putting "Grandchildren" at the top of her more current list. That shift influenced how she prioritized the rest of her values, which, in turn, helped her to stay true to herself. Self-care, which had no place at all before cancer, took a place at the top as well. Now she uses her values to make decisions about work, home environment, retirement, all with confidence, knowing she will honor what is most important.

Cancer seems to bring clarity to our values because it sheds light on what's truly important.

Marjorie's values were always there in her heart. Yours are too. Over the course of living life, some values become dormant and seemingly non-existent. Some have never been uncovered, named or acknowledged. In the face of a cancer journey, some values simply re-order in terms of priority. Cancer brings clarity to our values because it sheds light on what really matters to us.

Short of putting yourself through the wash like Marjorie though, how do you know what your values are now? We facilitate an exercise to help clarify values in our Cancer Journey Coach training workshops that we learned from The Co-Active Training Institute. We call it, "Best Life Experience," and we have included it for you at the end of the chapter.

Meanwhile, we want to tell you that in essence, when you live your values, it makes you happy. In fact, we say that living your values is the "key to happiness." Values work alongside the feedback mechanism of your emotions to serve as a guiding light. They can help you set boundaries, make decisions (from mundane to life-altering ones) and dream dreams.

Values tell you when you're in harmony with yourself. When you live in alignment with them, you tend to feel not only happy, but also more alive and filled with purpose. When you're upset or sad, it's likely that one of your top values is being ignored or "stomped on." Values help give you clarity about what is most important, and that clarity is powerful. Knowing your values frees you to become your own best Ally because you know deep inside, what it is that matters and gives meaning to your life.

Now you have been fully introduced to some of your most potent Allies, especially and most importantly, the ones within you. Please know that they are always but a thought and a choice away. In other words, the power is within you to be happy, no matter what your prognosis. Now, with full access to your Allies, you are ready to take the next step on this journey, a journey home to yourself. Keep moving forward, you are about to break through.

ADDITIONAL EXERCISES

Exercise: The Grief Bubble

When you grieve, you are acknowledging that you are letting go of something that matters to you. Grief is a memorial to a part of your life that no longer exists in the present moment. And as with arranging for a memorial service, experiencing grief benefits from some preparation. The following short exercise is designed to help you with the grieving process. Before you begin, sit in the quiet, or with music gently playing, and allow your heart to soften as you think about all that you have let go of, or are in process of letting go of, on your cancer journey. You may want to write your thoughts down. When you feel connected to your losses and your loving heart, begin:

The Grief Bubble:

1.   Imagine there is an iridescent bubble hovering just in front of you. It is filled with loving energy to transport your grief along with what you've let go of, to the place of honored and celebrated memories.

2.   Take a moment and with your arms outstretched and hands cupped, imagine releasing your grief so that it glides into this beautiful bubble.

3.   Say your good-byes and with a gentle blow from your lips, imagine the "grief bubble" floating off to the Land of Honored Memories.

4.   As you watch the grief bubble float away, feel and let go a bit more of the grief—letting go of what was once part of you, knowing that it does not serve you to hold onto it anymore, trust it will live on in the Land of Memories.

Wheel of Life

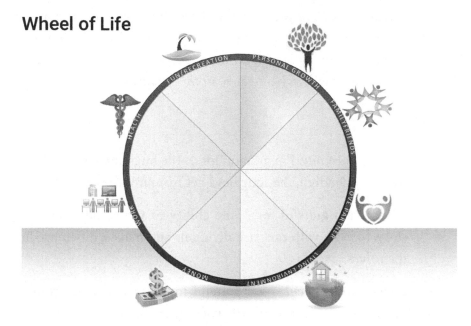

The Cancer Journey © All Rights Reserved

Exercise: Expanding Your Gratitude

There are many facets to our lives. For purposes of this exercise, let's say we have eight: family & friends, work, living environment, money, a love relationship (it can be the one you have with yourself), fun & recreation, personal growth, and health.

This exercise is about nurturing feelings of deep gratitude for all aspects of your life. As we tend to think of some areas as "better" than others—for example, our friendships might be more fulfilling than our work lives, it's really important to find something you can be grateful for in each of them. Gratitude leads to more gratitude.

Remember, gratitude is more than just being thankful. Love, joy, understanding and compassion are all mixed in. What's perhaps most powerful is the sense that you are not separate from anything nor anyone. Gratitude opens your heart so that you can know, deep inside, no matter what, that you belong.

Begin with one area of your life and then continue to the next area. Write down any and all of the things you are grateful for in this particular area, in this moment. As you do, allow yourself to be filled with the appreciation and delight of being alive *in this moment.*

Examples:

Friends & Family: I'm grateful for... the hugs and cuddles I get from my children, the snuggles I get from my 4-legged loves.

Work: I am grateful for... the ability to write and share my story, to work with cancer individuals and make a difference in their lives.

Living Environment: I am grateful for...my warm and comfy bed to rest in, nature out my back door that fills my soul and reminds me that I'm not alone.

Money: I am grateful for ...being able to buy the groceries that nourish my body, being able to donate to the women's shelter.

Love Relationship (Note: even if this means your loving relationship with yourself): I am grateful for ...someone to hold me when I need a hug, someone to connect with when I feel alone.

Fun & recreation: I am grateful for ... books that fill my soul and teach me new things, my morning hikes that stretch my limbs and energize my muscles.

Personal growth: I am grateful for...my spiritual practice that makes me feel closer to source, my garden that teaches me how natural it is to grow, heal and propagate.

Health: I am grateful for...my legs that carry me from room to room, my body's ability to heal itself.

Now try a wheel for yourself and see how your resonance rises with every expression of gratitude. Notice the Allies you see and feel all around you. Gratitude, felt and expressed, is an energizer.

Exercise: Discovering Your Values: Best Life Memory

After reading this brief description, we want you to close your eyes and think of a time in your life when everything was going well; a memory of living your best life. It can be a mere moment in time, a stage of life, or a significant event. For example, here's one of Keri's scenarios:

> *I see myself skiing in Lake Tahoe on a perfect sunny afternoon. I'm on the chairlift with my dear friend, Liana, and something gives us the giggles. We are snorting and crying with laughter and can barely get ourselves off the lift.*

The requirement is that it be a time in your life where you felt great about yourself and what you were experiencing. A time you felt fully present, operating on all levels. Once you have this image in your mind, take out a piece of paper or a notebook and set a timer for 5-minutes. Write it down, describing it as best you can. Go ahead. We'll wait.

For Keri, this was a Best Life Memory. And what makes it her best life memory is that many of her values were honored in that moment. So, let's see what's important to Keri based on this scenario? We can create her Values list: Nature. Friendship. Beauty. Being Physical/Health. Laughing/Humor.

However, one memory might not encompass all of your most important values, so if your list doesn't feel quite complete, you might want to work with another memory, or simply add the values you know are missing.

Here is another one of Keri's Best Life Memories:

> *My little peanut son is bundled and snuggled up beside me in the hospital bed. He'd just nursed for the first time, and I thought my*

heart was going to burst. I always considered myself to be a loving person. But I've never known a love like this. It's as if my heart and soul now exist outside of my body. I realize in that moment I would do anything for this little guy. I would literally give my life without a second thought. I'm experiencing my own capacity for love. It feels infinite. It feels miraculous.

What are the values you'd pull from this scenario? Values like Love, Motherhood, and Spirituality come to mind. If we'd only picked one of these scenarios, our values list would have been incomplete.

Now that you've written down your memories, go back and read what you wrote and either highlight or jot down what stands out to you as the important components. Create a list of values that stand out. Notice how you feel as you create your list. Don't be surprised if you feel energized or optimistic or moved, as Keri did when she wrote about her baby son. It's amazing how pinpointing what's most important carves a path of permission, possibility and motivation. And, yes, even joy.

CHAPTER SIX
THE BREAKTHROUGH STAGE

CONVENTIONAL WISDOM: "Breaking through" means you're through the worst of it, and now life can go back to normal.

CANCER JOURNEY INSTITUTE WISDOM: Breakthrough is your first solid sense that you are changed for the better by your cancer journey and you're not going back.

> "A Breakthrough is a moment in time when
> the impossible becomes possible."
> −TONY ROBBINS

Breakthrough: Stepping Into a New Reality

You are about to learn how to build upon the breakthroughs you are experiencing in relationship to yourself, your work, and those around you. You'll discover the form (the concrete details) of a desire isn't the same as the function (feeling/experience) of one, and how that opens the door to giving yourself some of what you long for, right now, whatever your circumstances. We'll help you plant dream seedlings. And we'll reveal the "magic in the telling" that happens when you share your breakthroughs with your Allies.

Shariann's Story: Health Is Wealth

Without notice or warning, it happens. A flash of awareness—"Your Health is your Wealth!" I hear the words so clearly in my head. "If you don't have your Health—body, mind, and soul—you don't have anything." Wow! I don't expect this, and I don't know what to do with it.

And yet, I feel the truth in these statements deep within. I feel lucky to have another chance at my life. This "After Cancer Treatment" phase allows me the chance to reflect on my cancer journey and the learning that brought me here.

In the stage of Innocence, before cancer entered my life, I thought chasing the American Dream was my North Star. Yet when I sensed something was "off" with my health, I began to feel that the American Dream was not mine, and that something more than just my health was "off." My childhood dreams, of being a teacher, of making a difference, were still alive and well and were making their way forward in my consciousness. In the Call, I had to let go of the past and the future and learn to stay present amidst the chaos. In Initiation, particularly during my fifth cancer journey, I found my voice, and used it when I decided not to continue treatment, even though my doctor said it could cost me days of my life. In The Pit, overwhelmed by fear, sadness, anger, and rage, I knew something had to change, and I learned how liberating it was to feel my feelings instead of pushing them away. This allowed me to see clearly my unhealthy pattern of "doing it all." In Allies, I learned to accept help, including allowing my husband to wash my hair and letting someone else take the lead. I stepped up as my own best Ally by giving myself permission to do whatever it took to care for myself, like take a long nap in the afternoon.

I have the deep knowing and appreciation that all I've been through has led me here, to this moment of realization that all the money, possessions, and accolades in the world will not give me what I really want from my life: love, peace, and connection. I want to know that I contribute to the whole in a positive way. I want to know that my life matters.

My palms start to sweat and my heart pounds with excitement. In this moment, my new and true North Star is forming around the revelation: "Health is Wealth." That, and this longing that is growing in me, to make a difference. It's about standing in the new "healthy" me with this body, this mind, this heart, and this spirit; all intertwined and feeling the richness of all that I get to give to this world, just because I'm me.

I want to shout it from the mountaintop; "I am rich because I know that I matter. It's not the stuff we accumulate, it's the positive impact we get to make, just by being true to ourselves!" This statement flows through my veins, and I feel the electric buzz that has me alive with possibilities.

Welcome to Breakthrough. This is a beautiful, tender time. It's also a very exciting one. As you go about the business of living, you find yourself coming up for air and noticing there really have been changes, particularly in your relationship with yourself. Even though things feel new and might still be a bit fragile, a new life is beckoning. You sense an opportunity for true and lasting change, and you want to trust it. So, you feed it by giving it your attention and commitment.

Instead of going back to normal, you are stepping into a new reality.

Perhaps you're experiencing flashes of a future that is peppered, if not filled, with hope. It's a bit like chasing after a butterfly in the woods: you catch glimpses of the beauty, and then it disappears again. Yet despite this now-you-see-it and now-you-don't experience, you know the butterfly is there. You can't go back into your past and un-see it. You are changing, becoming more of your true self. Instead of going back to normal, you are stepping into a new reality.

How Breakthroughs Happen

Breakthroughs feel instantaneous, but what's true is you have been building up to the "aha moments" throughout your cancer journey. Shariann's story tells us it was the deep-change work that she experienced along The Cancer Journey Roadmap that gave rise to her realization that "Your Health is Wealth!"

You, too, have been cultivating Breakthroughs all along, and now is when they become visible. You can see the signs of new ways of breaking through like new shoots in spring. Breakthroughs occur physically, mentally, and emotionally. And they can start small, like discovering that your body is waking up again and is beginning to fill with the sap of life and desire. Perhaps you notice fewer aches and pains, and you're able to be more present to your life, to your dreams and desires. And while it would be easy to forget how miraculous that is, given all you have been through, you don't ever want to take your freedom from pain for granted again.

You have changed, and you are not going back. Not only that, but, as we saw with Shariann, breakthroughs also reveal new possibilities.

The physical breakthroughs, even the tiny ones, seem to hold within them the possibility of even bigger internal changes. And while these changes range from subtle to obvious, each one is key to reclaiming the true you. The trick is to to pay them the attention they deserve. If not, they might slip through your fingers. But when you let them in, and we mean really let them in, by opening your heart wide to feel them right down to your toes, you begin to embody the knowledge that you are different.

In Breakthrough, you become aware that you not only don't want to, but you *can't* go back to the way things were. You aren't the same. Not physically, mentally, or spiritually. The past can't be recaptured because *you've* changed. Even if the outward circumstances of your life remain the same, you will experience them differently. This is not a bad thing, because there is so much more of you to discover, step into and live from.

It's also understandable if you fear *falling back* into old unhealthy patterns. What if the lessons you learned about things like self-care, compassion and kindness, fade? You've worked so hard and come so far. We want to assure you the lessons you've learned are there for you. One of the ways you've changed is that you can no longer turn your back on what's true, at least not for long. In other words, you can trust that the learning is in your bones forever, and that all of this is part of the process. Try to be gentle with yourself and allow things to unfold.

Breakthrough Is Not About Going Back to Normal

Shariann has a poignant memory about going back to work.

> *I am the main breadwinner, so I return to work without question. Sitting at my desk, I know it is time to re-engage with my job. I cannot seem to make myself to pick-up the phone; I cannot move a finger. I'm paralyzed. I can't do it. My hands won't move and my mind is spinning. "I don't want to do this!" a part of me screams inside.*

Without consciousness, I hear the voice in my head, "Is this what I want to do with my life? What is the purpose of selling more software? Does this matter to me? Oh My God! This work doesn't matter to me anymore and I can't pretend it does!" And, then it comes. "It's time." Time to find the work that has meaning to me; it is time to get off the hamster wheel and stop working for the money.

Shariann was having a Breakthrough moment. She realized that one of the ways she'd changed was she couldn't push herself to do what no longer had meaning. And she couldn't push her body through the fatigue.

Mary had a similar experience.

I still feel a little bit shaky, but it's been six weeks since the surgery and chemotherapy that ravaged my body. Damn my strong work ethic! I dust off my "favorite" black suit and pull on my new short and spiky wig that I bought before I lost so much weight. I feel like Nancy Reagan with poufy hair and a tiny body. I hate this wig, but I know that the office will be uncomfortable if I show up with my baldhead. Determined, I get into the car and head to the office. This feels so familiar and yet today, so foreign. My body feels a bit leaden, but my mind whips me to the office on autopilot.

Getting re-acclimated to my work surroundings, I notice, "Wow! Everything changed while I was gone!" The people I remember as colleagues seem to be just going through the motions, as if they aren't really present. What happened to them? Then I realize, they aren't the ones who changed. I am. I no longer feel like I can turn off my feelings and just buckle down to work. And I'm no longer willing to pretend. A moment of acknowledgement comes over me as I see how I pretzeled myself in order to fit in. I ran interference between top management and my team and burned myself out serving as a buffer.

My spine straightens and I sit up tall in my chair. One by one, team members start trickling into my office, asking me to help resolve one issue and another. I almost have to clap my hand over my mouth to stop myself saying, "I don't care! Don't you get it? I have stared death in the face and this treadmill of office life is not how I want to spend my precious time." It's my time. I realize I'm longing to step into what truly matters to me.

Both Shariann and Mary had breakthroughs when they realized how much they'd changed when they tried to go back to work. These aha moments were so undeniable, they both trusted and took steps to leave, and even though neither had a plan for what would come next. For Shariann that meant leaving her job after deep honest conversations, first with herself, then with her husband, then with her boss. Later, because she was willing to follow her truth, she began an entirely new career trajectory—one that eventually became The Cancer Journey Institute. Mary took out her paints and set up an easel by the window. Rekindling her passion bolstered her and led her to plan an early retirement.

Keri's Story was a bit different.

The sunshine on the deck draws me outside. I lean on the rails and let the warmth soak into my body. I've been in such pain lately. Not the physical kind, thank goodness. Yet somehow this feels worse. I've made errors and I feel guilty. But the worst part is instead of slowing down to check in, I've been beating myself up, demanding that I speed up, do more, and be better. And it's sent me into a shame spiral. This pain is all too familiar. I've fallen into some very old very deep pattern grooves. Grooves I thought had been filled in.

A metaphorical definition of insanity is when you keep walking down the same street, even though you know there's a sinkhole you keep falling into. I've managed to avoid this street for years, but for some reason, I'm back on it. With that realization, comes the thought, "Oh, Sweetie, you're only human! That street is familiar!"

The recognition almost makes me chuckle, and something lightens in my heart. I am human! Owning that somehow feels healing and freeing. It feels as if the sunshine has reached my insides. The warmth is my own understanding. It's sweetly soothing. So is my compassion.

I'm different since I had cancer. And I haven't given myself time to explore everything that means. I need time. I take a deeper breath and feel my heart expand. There's forgiveness here, but there's more. This is new. It's self-acceptance, something even more expansive than forgiveness. What's more, instead of banishing the part of myself who thinks I need to be perfect, I get to expand my heart to include her. This moment is an experience of who I'm becoming: a woman who is self-loving, who no longer seeks everyone's approval. I feel so grateful for this glimpse into a future embracing all of me. This Breakthrough moment is delicious! I am savoring the experience of true self-acceptance.

Keri's story reveals how cancer can open you to receive all parts of yourself—even those you don't like so much. Cancer is an opportunity to develop self-love and to set down the shame that often drives the desire to earn and prove. In letting go of shame, you begin to experience self-acceptance and the peace that comes with it.

Each of these stories illustrates how Breakthrough moments reveal more of the secret "why" of your cancer journey. Why it matters that you've been through what you've been through, why you've been both slowed down and stripped down, and why your future, even though you don't know all the details about it yet, feels utterly compelling. The call of your Soul is breaking through to find you.

Keri's Story: Breakthrough Feels like a Burst of Spring

I am a graduate student in my twenties when I experience my first "real" winter in Washington, D.C. As a California transplant, this is shocking to my system. Everything turns grey and cold and lifeless. Even though I know better, I can't imagine that the leaves will ever come back. One grey morning, I look out my still-frosty window to the tree branches just outside and see itty-bitty cherry buds. Some are opening revealing the bright pink about to burst out. The contrast to the grey-brown reality feels both stark and miraculous. I can almost taste it.

Hope. Hope is blooming out of the cherry tree. Even though the rest of the landscape is still dull and dead looking, this is an undeniable promise that life will again be filled with color and delight.

Breakthrough feels like beautiful pink hope bursting through the gray.

Breakthrough feels like beautiful pink hope bursting through the gray. It is like those cherry trees. Things might not look or feel all that different until you slow down enough to notice and appreciate the changes that are afoot, changes that can surprise and delight you as they emerge from the cracks of what was. Perhaps you are noticing a sweet blossoming within you, too. It feels fresh and bright, and it's beckoning you into your new life.

Here's what some of our clients have said about some of their own Breakthrough moments:

> *"I remember the moment I decided I wasn't going back to my corporate job, it felt like a lightning bolt of clarity," says Angela.*

Lynne shocked herself by setting a boundary. "The first time I said no to taking my son to school, it felt so automatic, I almost had to look around to see, 'who said that.'"

"I knew I had changed when I pulled into another lane and let another car pass me, even though I was running late. 'I'll get there when I get there,' Alex said to himself. 'This is not a matter of life and death.'"

John found he had lightened up considerably. "When laughter was my response to our new puppy piddling on my book manuscript, that was the moment I knew I had changed! Before cancer, there would have been hell to pay!"

The most important step is to recognize and acknowledge how you are different.

Breakthrough comes in many different forms. But however you experience it, it is vital that you recognize and acknowledge how you are different. You might first notice the changes in the quiet of your heart—and that is wonderful. But there is also something extraordinarily powerful about writing down what you see and feel or saying it out loud to a trusted witness. When you write the words down in a journal, or speak them to a friend or a coach, you are telling the world, and yourself, that your Breakthrough is real. We are fond of saying, "There's magic in the telling."

Shariann shared with her coach her Breakthrough of being willing to receive help, despite how challenging it was for her to accept it. Sharing this made her triumph more real. Together, Shariann and her coach were able to celebrate her achievement. What may have seemed like a small victory became transformational. Why? Because in sharing it, she embraced the change so that it became a part of her new self.

When Keri told her sister about her lapse in honoring herself, she could hear the pain in her own voice. Once acknowledged and spoken with a loving sister who was modeling non-judgment, she was free to forgive herself and commit more intentionally to self-care on all levels.

Again, "There's magic in the telling." But whom you tell is also very important. In Allies, you began to recognize the gift of people who champion you and care for you, without imposing their own agenda on you. These are the kind of Allies that you will want to gather around you as you experience the breakthroughs that naturally arise out of taking this deep, internal journey. When you share what is in your heart, with these kinds of Allies, your sense of confidence and clarity will grow. So avoid the naysayers, and lean into those that know how to support you in this next stage of your personal growth.

A Word to the Wise

While it's true you are changing, Breakthrough may not be the best time to *make big changes* in your life circumstances just yet. You're in the process of recalibrating. You are still catching your breath and finding your balance. In other words, generally speaking, now may or may not be the time to do things like get a divorce, move or quit your job. Shariann and Mary, had epiphanies of a different life possibility, but they didn't walk off their jobs that very second. Knowing that their souls were calling them elsewhere was the spark. Their willingness to stick with the feelings and stay curious eventually brought it to full flame.

You've already been through a huge change and an enormous amount of chaos. And if you try to do or change too much too soon, it will cause even more chaos. Yes, you want to make changes and you will. Breakthrough is the stage where you begin to see what wants to change and what is already changing. But it takes more time to be able to see a fuller picture, figure out finances, and set the structures in place to support deep change. That comes later, in Transformation.

Breakthrough is a time for noticing and being open to change.

Right now, we want to put it this way: Breakthrough is a time for noticing and being open to change. It is not time to restructure your whole life this very instant as much as it's an opportunity to receive whispered insights and, notice heart longings—take copious notes for changes you want to make in the future.

Breakthrough Is Where You Begin to Hear Your Soul's Calling

Breakthroughs are the moments where you begin to see your authentic self-bursting through. They are also accessible when you slow down and listen inwardly to the whispers of your soul. Molly's session with her coach, Alice, one of our Cancer Journey Coaches, illustrates what it can be like to hear your soul's calling.

Here's a snippet of their coaching session:

Molly: Most of my life, I thought that if I did what others wanted of me and worked really hard, I would be recognized and valued. I just wanted to be seen.

CJC Alice: I can tell from your quivering voice that this isn't working for you. What is doing what other's want from you and working really hard giving you?

Molly: (crying) It's giving me a headache and stress. It's making me exhausted. I believe that the stress is what caused my cancer. I feel so trapped.

CJC Alice: Let's slow this down. You're having some strong revelations here. Let's take them one at a time. How does it feel to realize that you've given your power of choice away to others to validate you?

Molly: It sucks! My parents taught me to be a good student in school; to do the assignment, get an 'A' and a 'Gold Star.' I believed that was how I was supposed to live my life. I don't want that kind of life anymore.

CJC Alice: How does this clarity feel?

Molly: It feels freeing. I feel like I can actually take a deep breath. I didn't realize until this moment that I was just being a 'good' soldier. Cancer has shaken up my life and stopped me in my tracks.

CJC Alice: I hear you on so many levels. Cancer has broken you open and given you the opportunity to see and stop a long-held pattern, a pattern that was not allowing you to live a life that honored who you really are. You feel the depths of how giving your power away has impacted you. I also hear and see a fire within you that is growing. What does that fire want?

Molly: It wants me to come alive. It wants to burn away the pain and shame of me not standing up for myself and asking for what I want. Hmmm…it's making me feel powerful like I could be a 'ball of fire.'

CJC Alice: Yes, Miss Ball-of-Fire. What can you see from here?

Molly: I see possibilities. I see freedom. I see a future for me and about me. I see myself approving of what I do and how I do it. Wow! I see me!

CJC Alice: I think we just found the You that has been transformed by cancer. Let's see how this new Molly wants to show up in the world.

Molly needed the time and space to explore her ruminations, and her Cancer Journey Coach, Alice, was able to slow her down and mirror back what Molly was saying and seeing. The awareness of what didn't work for her anymore, or really ever, drew her to look deep within her soul to find what does. And the clarity of her soul's calling opened future possibilities. Breakthrough is like finding a new metaphor. Molly's "Ball of Fire" has such a different energy to it than being a good girl. Breakthrough has us discover these amazing new touchstones for who we are. Like Shariann's mantra, "Health is Wealth" or what Keri came to call her anchor, "True Self-Acceptance." It's powerful to start looking at our lives through the energy of these new lenses.

Breakthrough is a Wonderful Time to Dream Dreams.

Dreaming gives your life vitality.

Hearing your soul's calling requires quieting the noise in your mind. Because of your recently bolstered self-respect, the volume was turned down on the voice of your wounded ego, and you have set boundaries between yourself and the projections and expectations of others. What that means is that you can now more easily hear your soul's voice. It calls to you through the whispers of your dreams and desires. And you feel a longing to answer the call.

Some of us respond to this calling by diving deeply into a pool of exploration. Others respond by putting their toes into several different pools before diving in. Let your heart and soul guide you. There is no right or wrong way, just *your* way to discover more of *you*.

Dreams are imagined experiences of your desires. Whispers are the seedlings of what your dreams can become. If you listen to what the whispers are telling you, they can be a powerful guide. For example, you may dream of exploring a long-held passion of writing a book or living in community with loved ones. You might desire to love and accept yourself for who you truly are or long to take a risk without being paralyzed by worry or failure.

None of this is dependent on your prognosis, by the way. Whatever your future holds and however long that future stretches, know that your new self has been awoken and so has your connection to soul. That is more important than manifesting a particular circumstance. So right now, it's time to honor that by giving attention to your emerging dreams and desires—it is the yearnings themselves that will give your life wings. Even still, you may have glimpsed new possibilities and new changes may have already begun to take root. Now you're going to expand this by intentionally using your imagination to visualize and experience different aspects of your desired future.

The act of dreaming gives your life vitality. It's the breath that fills your lungs, the water that quenches your thirst. Dreaming ignites your spirit, opens your mind, and lifts your emotions to a higher vibration. It acts as a magnet, attracting more of what you desire, and it begins with one of the most powerful and provocative questions you can ask yourself: What do I want?

Your soul is speaking to you in its preferred language: longing and desire.

Some of us hear that question and get inspired as ideas and details flow from our imagination, "I want a pink house with blue shutters, three bedrooms and a rose garden." Others feel overwhelmed by its vastness. "I want…um… world peace?" Some of us dream in visual and sensual detail, others dream in feelings and essence. Please be assured, all of this is great news and all of it is important and valid. It means your soul is speaking to you in its preferred language: longing and desire.

Whether your desires come in pictures, paragraphs, sensations, or essences, we find it helpful to use a structure to break it down and make it less overwhelming. We borrowed and then adapted ours from The Co-Active Institute called, "The Wheel of Life." You saw it in Allies. To remind you, here are the categories it contains: health; love partner (this can also be you); friends/family; money; career/work; living environment (where you live, people around you, etc.); personal growth; fun and recreation.

Breaking dreams down into these categories, rather than trying to come up with one grand vision makes dreaming a lot less intimidating. It also allows you to begin with either specific details or with essence and emotion—also known as form and function, respectively. We've included exercises at the end of this chapter to play more with the elements of form vs. function. But right now, we're going to share another structure with you that focuses, at least initially, more on form—the specific, detailed picture. As you go through this exercise, keep in mind that your psyche doesn't know the difference between an actual circumstance, and one that is clearly imagined. Even if you can't physically realize a dream you have, don't let that deter you. Your inner self will feel as though it has really happened.

We call this process "*Creating D.R.E.A.M. Seedlings.*" Like the Disney lyric says, "*A Dream is a wish your heart makes,*" dreams live in our hearts. They become real when we seed them. The important part is allowing your dream to take shape by tuning into the feelings and pictures your heart is showing you. In this way you create a *seedling* of a dream. A seedling you will nurture over time until the dream blossoms into full fruition.

We have a framework within our D.R.E.A.M. Seedling Process to help you determine whether the dream is truly your heart's desire, versus something you think you "should" want.

D.R.E.A.M. represents:

   D = **Desire**—You want this.

   R = **Real**—You can imagine yourself really having this.

   E = **Excitement and Expectation**—Thinking about it excites you and you have a positive expectation that it will happen.

   A = **Alive**—It is a living vision, and it brings you alive.

   M = **Moving and Motivating**—You find the dream moving and it motivates you to move forward.

Here's how it works. In each of the eight categories we named above, you can create a *D.R.E.A.M. Seedling*. A scene in the future, a moment in time where you are living inside your dream, a lot like your Best Life Memory, which you played with in Allies, except it's in the future. Choose whatever timeframe you like. We suggest within one year because it's far enough in the future, but it's immediate enough to feel obtainable. Choose whatever timeframe feels right for you.

Let's walk through an example, starting with the category of HEALTH. The first step is, to ask yourself, what would be my ideal HEALTH scenario within 12 months?

Here's a possible answer, using the idea of a D.R.E.A.M. Seedling:

> *I am walking the trails of Yosemite with ease. I'm going at "my" pace and feeling the air fill my lungs and my strong muscles moving in unison. I'm on an incline and notice that I am gliding up it with minimal effort. I can sense the trees feeding me clean fresh oxygen, and my footsteps help to move the fallen seeds into new areas for germination. My soul is delighting in the connection and symbiosis with nature. My spirit is alive and is bringing me more alive.*

In this D.R.E.A.M. Seedling, you can feel how physical, mental, emotional and spiritual health all combine. Now, let's look back to the D.R.E.A.M framework, to do a sort of litmus test.

D – Desire: Do you want this adventure in Yosemite?

R – Real: Can you see and feel it in your imagination?

E – Exciting, Expectation: Does it evoke excitement and can you expect it will happen? (Note: this is all about the emotional experience of expectation and doesn't mean anything about logic!)

A – Alive: Does this moment bring your spirit alive?

M – Moving, Motivating: Does this snapshot moment move you? Are you motivated to make it happen?

If your answer is "YES" to all of these, then it is a true D.R.E.A.M. Seedling.

It's like a stake in the ground that says, "As long as I'm alive, I'm choosing to live!"

The point is, dreaming and creating D.R.E.A.M. Seedlings make life feel compelling and vital. Having an emotion-packed picture, a vision of a future where you are reaching and stretching beyond where you are today in Breakthrough can provide a solid North Star to draw and guide you forward. While it is true that your power is in the present moment, having a compelling future vision calls you to continue on your path. Not only that, but D.R.E.A.M. Seedlings inspire the energy and excitement that come with having a Compelling Vision for your Future. Remember, your psyche doesn't know the difference between a vision and reality. Even when you're just envisioning yourself hiking in Yosemite, your inner being is responding as if you actually *were* hiking in Yosemite. It's like you're proclaiming to the universe, "As long as I'm alive, I'm choosing to live!"

We've noticed, working with cancer individuals, that they can be reluctant to dream about the future for fear of being crushed by "false hope" or the belief that "it will never come true." So, if the knowledge that your brain doesn't know the difference between a dream and your imagination doesn't help, the *Form and Function Exercise* at the end of the chapter will come in handy. We will explain this process in vivid detail but suffice it to say, right now, that every dream has a function, purpose, or essence. And we believe you can have the essence or experience of what you want right now, no matter your circumstances or prognosis.

Breakthrough is the beginning of knowing and accepting that you are *changed*. You have confronted your mortality, and you are being invited to embrace life, a life you don't ever want to take for granted, no matter how long or short. This is what it feels like to wake up.

The great news is if you find yourself falling back to sleep, your Allies, both internal and external, will wake you up again, like Keri's did. They play a major role as you continue to grow, expand, and love yourself along your journey. You are just beginning to integrate all of the changes.

Right now, standing here in Breakthrough, take a moment to feel, experience and celebrate. You've gone through so much. You've changed so much. And you are still changing. Take it in and receive it. You're not going back to who you were. Breakthrough carries within it a contract with your soul. That contract says you are making a commitment to live authentically, to receive more love and more joy. As you stand here, notice: you don't want to take your life for granted. You are being awakened, and you never want to fall back asleep.

ADDITIONAL EXERCISES

Exercise: Journaling Breakthroughs

Journaling allows us to get the swirl of thoughts, feelings and ideas in our minds and hearts onto a piece of paper or computer screen. The goal is to allow yourself time and space (we recommend at least 10 minutes daily, at the end of your day—or the beginning if that's when you have more juice) to honor your Breakthroughs by recording them.

- Set a timer for how long you want to give yourself (10, 20, 30 minutes)

- Get settled in a quiet space. Use the prompts below and write whatever wants to come. Know that this dedicated time and space can provide the structure to become aware of some of the Breakthrough moments that are occurring. They may even inform future D.R.E.A.M. Seedlings.

- Use one of these writing prompts if needed:

  - What was a highlight about today?

- What was different about today?

- What was different about you today?

- What is emerging from you? What longs to be expressed?

- What do you want to say, feel, or do in this moment?

D.R.E.A.M. Seedling Exercise
(using the "Wheel of Life" structure)

Use the chart below as a guideline to write out a "Seedling" for each "slice of life" category.

On a separate sheet of paper, or in your journal, begin writing.

Slice of Life	D.R.E.A.M. Seedling
Health	
Friends & Family	
Love Partner	
Work	
Money	
Living Environment	
Personal Growth	
Fun & Recreation	

Form & Function Exercise

Our desires come to us in one of two ways. Either we want *a specific physical "thing"* or *form*, like a car, a home, a new outfit, or specific activity. Or we know we want *to experience a specific slice of life and/or to feel a certain way.* This is what we call the *function. Functions* can be expressed in any number of *ways:* experience—like learning something new, having a release, playing, or creating beauty; or a feeling—like openness, excitement, connection, love. Depending on how your desires come to you initially, you can start with either *form* (concrete details) or *function* (feelings and experience).

To help with differentiating form and function, here's an example—

THE FUNCTION: *Having light in my room.*

THE FORM: *Turning on a lamp, lighting a candle, opening the shade to allow sunshine in, or igniting a fire that provide the "light."*

FORM: The *physical thing* (e.g. A lamp, a candle, the sun, a fire)

FUNCTION: The *experience* provided by the physical thing (light in my room)

Once again, when you want "some *thing*" (*the form*), it is because you want the *function* or experience you believe that "some *thing*" will give you. This is true before cancer, during cancer, and after cancer. It's particularly helpful to remember this when you have cancer, because you may not have the physical ability to obtain or do the specific "some-thing" in the *form*.

As we said earlier, everything has a *function*. And once you determine—what it is you want to experience from the *form* you desire, you suddenly have many more options for satisfying your desires. As you can imagine, some forms are a lot more accessible than others.

For example, if the "something" you want is the nature walk we referred to in this chapter, but you cannot physically take a walk out in nature in this moment, you can still have the *function* of what the walk in nature will give you. The question to ask to determine its function is, "What will walking in nature give me?" The answer might be something like, "I want to be with the trees and plants." Ask again until you get to more of an essence or experience (the function), like "I want to feel connected to the natural world." Or "I want to be with the beauty and wonder of Mother Earth." Then, you can explore other ways (forms) to have that experience (function). In this case, forms other than taking a nature walk could be watching a *National Geographic* show, reading a book about birds or animals, or planting a window box garden. Each of these examples provides an experience of connecting with the power and beauty of nature.

When you're creating your D.R.E.A.M. Seedling Moments, we want you to know that you do not have to give up your dreams or wait for "some day" to have the experience you want. We suggest the following steps:

- Take a look at each one of your D.R.E.A.M. Seedlings.

- Find its *function*. How does that Seedling make you feel? What does the Seedling "give you" in terms of feelings? What's the experience you want to have?

- Then, list other possible forms that come to mind.

- Discover and choose a FORM you can give yourself today.

The point of this exercise is to be able to address your needs and desires and to feel alive and part of the world, now. Allow yourself to have a piece of your dream, today.

Exercise: Committing to your Soul Contract

Once you have slowed down to listen to the whispers and you're clear on your Breakthrough, you'll want to "lock-in" the awareness. Here is a ritual we often do in our trainings and with our clients to mark this important event.

1. Begin by writing down what you want to commit to. Some examples might be: "I commit to speaking my truth." Or "I commit to checking in with myself before saying 'yes' to others' requests. They can also be broad, like, "I commit to being more loving with myself," as long as you know what that means.

2. Create or imagine a line on the ground in front of you (note: if you are feeling unwell or have limited physical space, feel free to do this in your imagination)

3. While standing on "this side" of the line, declare aloud what it is you are committing to. Remember, there is magic in the telling, even if it is only to yourself.

4. Once you have made your declarations of commitment, step over the line. It might be fun to imagine a group of your Allies (they can be physical or non-physical) cheering you on, on the "other side" of the line.

5. Allow yourself to receive the commitment you've made. Feel the realness of this commitment in your body. Celebrate it: e.g. do a celebration dance, create a crafty totem that reminds you every day, or write it on your bathroom mirror.

6. You've come a long way. Give yourself a big hug!

CHAPTER SEVEN
THE TRANSFORMATION STAGE

CONVENTIONAL WISDOM: Transformation is the end of your journey. You are now transformed back into the healthy person you were and can return to the life you had before cancer.

CANCER JOURNEY INSTITUTE WISDOM: A Cancer Journey changes you. Now it's time to embrace your dream of a greater life as you step into your truest and most powerful self.

"Transformation is a process, and as life happens there are tons of ups and downs. It's a journey of discovery."
—RICK WARREN

Transformation: Celebrating The New You

This chapter offers you insights into, how your Cancer Journey has changed you, and how those changes can manifest in your life in powerful ways. It addresses The Shadow of Cancer—the fear that it may yet come back—and shows you how to confront those dark moments head on, without piling on the fear. Above all, it invites you to see Transformation as an ongoing process that, when you engage with it, reaps greater and more miraculous benefits over time.

Shariann's Story: Embracing The New Me

Still absorbed in my breakthrough "My Health is My Wealth" epiphany, I take a pause and rest on my comfy grey sofa and gaze out of the window at the expanse of hills stretching across the horizon. I used to think that "health" was only about my body and would often do a quick scan and quiz: Did I have the energy and stamina to walk to the top of the Pacifica Beach hill to enjoy the crashing waves and ocean skimming surfers? When was the last time I had a leaky nose and never-ending cough from a cold? And, yes even, was I pooping regularly? These were all indicators of "health" to me.

The awareness that my mental, emotional and spiritual health were not part of my definition of health, pre-cancer, makes my eye twitch. Sure, I "thought" about my mental health, but I'm a "glass half full" kind-of-gal. Yup, positivity is my #1 strength, but I now realize that I contain many more qualities than that—like kindness and self-compassion. It's as if my eyes have opened and I'm seeing through a new lens. There is something growing so profoundly and quickly inside of me. Health and wealth... hmmm.

As I warm my hands around my tea cup and take a slow, thoughtful sip, the truth of what I know rolls in: My body may not be as strong as it was, but my spirit and heart are so much more open and willing; my mind may forget things, a carry-over from chemo brain, but it knows what is true and honest to me; and my emotions are my friend, my own personal feedback system that lets me know when and where to pay attention. In this quiet and soothing moment, I am embracing all of me, this conglomeration of my past, my present and stepping solidly into my glorious future.

I close my eyes for a moment to really take in who I am, in this moment, and my arms automatically surround me in my own loving hug. I love me. Let me say that again, I love me! And, as I embrace this new version of me, I lean into her and allow images, visions, and dreams of what she wants to do, and how she wants to share all of herself—this fabulous new, powerful woman.

We often call Cancer, "The Big 'C'" for this reason. That C stands for **Change**.

Congratulations. You have arrived at Transformation, the last stage of your cancer journey. Take a moment to reflect and celebrate, as you become aware of the immensity of the odyssey you have taken, the inner work you have done, and the changes that have taken place.

Transformation, after all, is defined as "a thorough or dramatic change; a metamorphosis." We often call Cancer, "The Big 'C'" for this reason. That C stands for *Change.* You caught glimpses of that change in Breakthrough. You seeded dreams and felt them stirring inside you. Now is the time to seize those dreams and make them real. Transformation isn't just a concept or an idea—it is more concrete than that. It is when your dreams begin to materialize into a new and more authentic way of living.

Keri's Story: My Transformation Is Still Unfolding

A tear slips past my cheek and runs into my ear. Turning to reach for a tissue, I feel the sheets crackle under me as only hospital sheets will do. And I know them well, having finished treatment for breast cancer only a year and a half ago. They've just unhooked me from the EKG Monitor. I haven't had a heart attack, thank God. But how did I get here?

Just an hour ago, my heart was beating so hard in my chest it was visible. Madly trying to finish an email, I knew I was tired, but the adrenaline helped me to override the fatigue and push through. Just keep going, I say to myself. It will subside. But it didn't. So now I'm here at the ER. What happened to the promises I made to myself? What happened to being self-honoring?

Days and weeks later, I'm still processing this. Grief and remorse wash over me. What happened to the commitments I made during treatment? What happened to the breakthroughs I had about how much I matter? What happened to loving and accepting myself without apology that gave me an experience of inner peace I'd longed for my entire conscious life? Where was it all now? Where am I, now? There's something familiar and awful here... Oh... It hits me... I abandoned myself. I'd climbed onto my own Victim-Warrior seesaw and got trapped in martyr. My joy and passion for this work morphed into slave driving have to's.

As understanding dawns, my heart hurts, and I feel such compassion for my Victim—a wounded part inside of me, a part that couldn't take any more of this love and beauty stuff! "Yeah, yeah, now, get back to work." At that point, I stopped listening and started driving myself.

My self-abandonment had some unintended negative impact, and as I write this, I'm still processing my remorse. Meanwhile, being in the ER had me stop and listen more deeply. Now I can hear the whispers of my Soul again. The whispers say, "I'm craving space. Space to integrate my journey and explore what's next. To remember and experience joy and beauty."

Part of my Transformation, I realize, is forgiving myself for what feels like a ginormous transgression of forgetting to put myself first. Before cancer, I would have "hung myself on the hook for months"—years even, beating myself up. Now, there are tears of remorse and compassion as I face the truth, so much more quickly than in the past. Gone is the slave-driven martyr who says I'm undeserving, that I need to earn my worth.

What's different now is that I'm willing to give myself what I need: space and time. My body relaxes at the thought of it. What I really need is to feel loved and accepted, and I know enough to know it has to come from me. I wrap my arms around myself and take in my own hug. Tears well. It moves me to give this to myself. I matter, and so do my needs. I pause to let that in. Before my cancer journey, I wouldn't have acknowledged this. This change might seem subtle but, for me, it's profound.

I don't know where my transformation journey will lead me. But I can feel the edges of something, a calling of my Soul that feels like a deep longing. Will I expand my healing work to a new level? I want to claim myself as a healer—a facilitator of healing, because I know healing resides within. It feels like another metamorphosis wants to happen, either that or a greater understanding of the one that has already taken place. I don't know what that means or where it will end up. I do know that I long to explore it. And I know that right now, transformation for me is the willingness to give myself the space and time I need to explore what comes next.

Transformation does not happen all at once, as Keri's story shows us. It is a disorderly process that unfolds over time—two steps forward and one back. Still, Transformation has a very different quality to it than the early stages of your journey. Even the questions you carry in your heart have changed.

Remember in The Call when we said that when we get a cancer diagnosis, it's very human to ask, "Why? What did I do or not do to cause this?" Compare these with the questions that arise from your vantage point of Transformation. "What have I learned and discovered? How have I changed? Who am I now? How do I want to and choose to live?" Keri is clearly still answering these questions, and that's part of her ongoing process of transformation. But it's important that you also give yourself time and space to dig deeper and discover more. And, at the end of this chapter, you'll find an exercise to do just that.

How You've Changed—Knowing You Matter

You might notice in Transformation that your values, needs and desires have shifted—the changes you noticed in Breakthrough have become even more pronounced. Whether or not they're the same as before, one thing feels certain. Now they refuse to be ignored. This is a result of knowing how much you matter.

For example, Shariann had to grapple with the blank slate of ending treatment and no longer being willing to work in an environment she felt lacked meaning for her. If she hadn't valued herself and, hadn't known how much she mattered, she would not have given herself permission to act on her desires. She wouldn't have felt she had the luxury to entertain the option of leaving her work, especially when she didn't know what was next. Her transformation—knowing she mattered—originated from within her heart, and it showed up when she gave herself space and allowed herself to get quiet. Then, little by little, the answers came, and the path was shown. Her passion was awakened, and she felt a calling. A calling so strong it couldn't be denied.

This is a gift you discover at this stage. Because you now know you matter, you are willing to stop and not only listen but also honor what your heart is saying, no matter how faint or foreign its messages may seem. We want to assure you that even if it doesn't seem to make any logical sense, you can trust that your soul will guide you. In other words, the path will be shown.

"I'm different now because of what I've been through," says Shariann. "It's more than physical. I absolutely *had* to do this meaningful work. And my Soul's voice got louder, the more I listened. First, I found the coaching profession, and then I realized I wanted to help those who are having their own cancer journeys. There was a knowing inside and when I heard it, I knew this was my path."

This is the most exciting part of Transformation: discovering who you have become and the new trajectory you're on.

This is the most exciting part of Transformation: discovering who you have become and the new trajectory you're on. While in many ways, you're the same person you were when you first stepped onto the roadmap, it's important to acknowledge and appreciate how you have grown and evolved. We've included a visualization at the end of the chapter to introduce and guide you through this sweet encounter with your "new" self.

Meanwhile, here's what some of our Cancer Journey Coaches have said about their own experiences of Transformation.

For Amy, *"This journey has enriched who I am and has allowed me to become my truer self."*

"The transformation for me was that I stand in my own unique shoes and embrace who I am in a way I did not before." says Maggie, *"I've gained confidence and openness and willingness to*

explore my own vulnerability with deeper love and acceptance of myself."

Denise says, "I recognized the areas of my life where I was in the Victim-Warrior mode. And through acceptance and growth, moved into accepting a Bigger Picture of my life."

According to Susanna, "… I feel much more confident now because [I have] many tools…"

"This was the opening to my spiritual growth," says Martina.

You, too, have made profound and beautiful changes. You will see this as you increasingly welcome and integrate your transformed self. The important thing is to stay conscious and present by taking it one dream, one step, one moment at a time.

The Bittersweet Price of Wisdom

Part of being in Transformation is both looking back at who you were and reflecting on who and where you are now. As you continue to grow and change in Transformation, you also notice the contrasts and paradoxes. And they are bittersweet. For example, you've gained so much wisdom and insight, but you've also suffered losses, from mild to extreme. And they need to be honored and integrated too.

One of the most bittersweet losses brought on by your cancer journey is that of your innocence. Once that bubble of innocence popped, you knew you would never be the same. Knowing and accepting this can be sobering. You have faced the cruel reality that "bad things," like a cancer diagnosis, can and do happen, even to you. The innocence of feeling immune to death and disease no longer exists. But on some level, you also know that losing your innocence has opened more space for bigger dreams and possibilities, and that your experience is the price you've paid for learning to love yourself and your life just a little more fiercely.

"Yes," you think. "Now I'm ready to leave cancer behind, as a thing of the past. I am ready to move on."

But we would be remiss if we didn't tell you that the loss of innocence has also left room for a certain and very real fear: the fear that your cancer will spread or that it will recur. Fear of recurrence is so universal we've given it its own name: the Shadow of Cancer.

The Shadow of Cancer

Like your physical shadow, cancer's shadow is always in the background, whether it's scarily big and lurking right behind you, or small and barely noticeable. In other words, at times you're very much aware of it, at other times not so much, but it never truly goes away. Sometimes it feels like it's hovering right over your shoulder, like when you are about to have a routine scan or doctor's appointment.

On the other hand, when you're feeling strong, resourced, and engaged in living, it fades or becomes invisible. Even so, the slightest ache or pain can pull the darkness right back. *The Shadow* is the fear of loss, the fear that life, as you know it, will be taken away, even though it has not happened and there is no logical reason to believe it will. And something we know about the fear of loss is that it increases when there's more love in the mix. As your capacity to love yourself and others expands, your attachment to your life, to people, and nature, grows. The fear of losing your connection to this expanded life is so sweet that the thought of losing it is painful.

Over the course of this journey, love has definitely increased, your *self*-love has increased. That's good news. The other good news: the fear of loss can be managed.

Remember the recipe for dealing with fear stories and the monsters under the bed you learned in Initiation and The Pit? We're going to apply it here, because the best way to deal with your own *Shadow of Cancer* is to get to know it. Face it, and stop pushing it away or making up stories about it, or worrying or judging your self for having this fear.

All that does is make it bigger and scarier. Have you ever noticed that a shadow can look larger and more frightening than the actual thing? But like the monster under the bed, once you face it, it disappears, or at the very least, shrinks.

Here is a short, helpful exercise for facing the shadow.

Exercise: Coming to Terms with the Shadow of Cancer

Settle in comfortably and allow the Shadow to fall on you. Don't hide from it or diminish it. However big or dark it appears, let it be. When you are ready, take your time responding to the following questions. You can give your answers out loud or write them in your journal. The most important thing is to put your thoughts into words. Speaking your answers to a cherished friend and Ally can be particularly healing.

1. "What do you notice about the shadow? How does it look and/or feel?"
2. "What story is the Shadow of Cancer telling me?" "How is it threatening me?"
3. Then you can ask, "Is this really true?"
4. Followed by, "What do I know to be true?"
5. And, "What do I want to say to my Shadow of Cancer?"

Facing your Shadow of Cancer will calm your fears. We haven't met a single cancer survivor who hasn't encountered the shadow. The great news is that while your shadow can stop you in your tracks, it is also a natural part of the transformation process. When you accept this, you also come to realize that the Shadow is temporary and can be dealt with. In facing the dark, you start to move back into the light.

Transformation is a Process

Transformation is an exciting stage of the journey. But it doesn't always show up in big changes and grand gestures, even though you may be tempted to jump in with both feet right away. Know and trust that transformation begins on the inside. It's a process.

You've already discovered, transformation is wonderful and messy and miraculous. And getting here to Transformation is worth everything you've been through. As your travels on the Cancer Journey Roadmap have shown you, discovering and embodying your powerful self is a process unto itself.

Transformation almost feels like a second chance at living the life you want because you've come full circle. Instead of making promises like the ones you made right after diagnosis, "I'll eat perfectly from now on!" "I will be kind to myself." "I'll never take my life for granted." You can now feel that your life is *filled with* promise—the promise of a life full of love, passion, truthfulness, compassion, forgiveness, and your own beautiful humanity.

Remember the stories Shariann and Keri shared in Innocence? They've come back around. Now Shariann is both that teacher and writer because she had the courage to stay open and vulnerable to cancer as a pathway to deep transformation.

Keri's heart opening allows her to receive more love from herself. Remember that little girl who took care of her stuffed animals back in Innocence? Now she can give herself the love and nurturing she always longed for and given so readily to others. And in opening to receive more love, she now loves others even more deeply and more readily. Both Keri and Shariann's experiences were transformational at a soul level.

Transformation shows up in subtle ways that make a big difference.

We hope we've made it clear, but in case we haven't: Transformation is *not* about perfection. It is about honoring yourself as a growing, changing being, day-by-day, more and more. Honoring yourself means loving and embracing everything that's unfolding, including your feelings, your passions, your thoughts, and ideas. This isn't something you'll do 100% perfectly, of course. But, as Keri's and Shariann's stories illustrate, you now have self-acceptance and forgiveness ready to bring you back home to yourself and your desired path.

Transformation shows up in subtle ways that make a big difference. You find new behaviors have become habits, like when Keri started asking her husband for what she wanted. Or when Shariann gave herself permission to swing out there with an innovative dream. Transformation looks like consistently listening and responding to your body, your thoughts, and your energy. These small, subtle, and brave changes have a big compounding effect.

Transformation is where you can finally dismount the exhausting Victim-Warrior seesaw and embrace life from a more self-aware and self-loving perspective. From this place, you can see when you inadvertently climb back onto the seesaw. You won't always realize it right away, like you saw with Keri's story. But the good news is, once you see it, you can choose to get off. And we do mean *choose.*

Giving yourself Permission

Transformation also means you have *permission* to live the life that you *want,* instead of one you thought you *should* have. The life you want is coming closer and clearer because you are doing and discovering what brings you joy and honors your own personal values. You've also gained courage and strength during your cancer journey. Courage and strength you can call upon as you step into your new life.

Speaking of having a new life, remember the coaching interaction between Molly and her Cancer Journey Coach, Alice? Molly's breakthrough was the epiphany that she was living for others' approval and validation.

Her transformation is illustrated in this coaching interaction.

CJC Alice: You've been getting acquainted with Miss Ball-of-Fire, for a while. Tell me about her, now.

Molly: She is still elusive sometimes. She comes in and then she is far away.

CJC Alice: That's so understandable. It can take time. Let's see if we can bring her closer now. I'd like you to take a deep breath, and on the exhale, close your eyes and put your hand on your heart. We're going to create space for Miss Ball-of-Fire to show up. (Pause) What can you share from here?

Molly: She's kind of bossy—knows what she wants, and she likes to tell people how she feels and what to do. And she doesn't have a lot of patience. My family is almost shocked when I'm in Miss Ball-of-Fire mode because normally I'm much more concerned about what they want, and my wants are usually second or last. I think I saw my daughter smiling the other day when I said that I wanted to go to the flower market and asked who wanted to come with me. I would typically have asked what others were doing first, and then I'd see if there was time for me to squeeze in what I want. Did I ever mention that I love flowers? When I was little, I used to make bouquets from the flowers in our yard and tie them with one of my colorful hair ribbons to give to my neighbors. I loved the smiles and joy it brought to everyone.

CJC Alice: It sounds like a passion from your past is showing up in this powerful and free woman. I'm getting that you're reclaiming a part of yourself that has been pushed down by responsibilities. What do you get when you go to the flower market?

Molly: Hmmm…there is this sense of peace that comes over me. The beauty of the different florals and the abundance of vibrant greenery seem to spark a creativity that my life has been lacking. I've been playing with some flowers that I bought and I'm realizing that I have a really good eye for creating exotic arrangements. It's like it just flows out of me. I can see the bird of paradise and immediately I want to add in white jasmine and then add in some yellow mums nestled in vibrant green fern leaves and it's an explosion of color, scent, and texture. I made an arrangement for my sister-in-law to give to her mother and they were posting pictures of it all over Facebook. I'm even sketching designs in my free time.

CJC Alice: There's something here, Molly. You come alive when you talk about creating floral arrangements and the impact it has on others. Your energy fills the entire room. What do you want to do with this knowing?

Molly: Yes. A secret dream is unfolding. I talked to Ben about what I'm feeling and thinking. I want to do this; I want to try my hand at doing this as a side business to start. I feel like I've reconnected or awakened a part of me that was asleep. I like who I am when I'm creating. It feels like my personal expression.

In her coaching session, Molly connected with and became aware of the part of herself who now has *permission* to be authentic. That permission allowed her creativity to flow so that she could delight in her passions and talents. Her passion for exotic floral design became clear and now she's inspired to put together a business plan. As her confidence increases, she finds it easier to embrace her powerful, alive self. Today, Molly doesn't need to look elsewhere for validation, her brilliance and self-worth glow from the inside out.

Living in Transformation requires trusting the process

Remember, "*Power is the willingness and ability to act.*" By increasing her willingness to put herself first, Molly is not only embracing her transformation, she's stepping into her power. Living in Transformation requires trusting the process.

As you can see, in Transformation, you are free to embrace life on your own terms, which means living out your dreams. Now you get to decide, moment to moment, how you will walk the path to making those dreams real. As you begin to launch into your new life, you will feel excitement or trepidation, but most likely, both. So, know that as long as you are committed to being and becoming more of your authentic self, you cannot go wrong. Trust that backslides and roadblocks don't mean there's anything amiss, they are simply part of the process of growing into this new you. All and any of the stages on the roadmap are worth revisiting. But you'll be doing so at a higher octave.

You can trust the process even more now that you are able to accept yourself no matter what. Self-acceptance and trusting the process will come in handy when you find yourself off course or reverting to old habits. The tools you now have, along with the learning you've gained from your cancer journey will only serve to strengthen your ability to venture forward and keep growing into the life you dream of—a life that is sustained by love, trust, and hope.

The world would be less whole if you were not here; not because of what you do, but simply because you exist.

The love, trust and hope we are speaking of come from the belief that you are on your own unique Soul's Journey, and that you are unconditionally loved by the Divine (whether you call it God, Goddess, Jesus, the Universe, All that Is, Source, or whatever name you choose.) Even when you don't feel it, you are important and connected. The world would be less whole if you were not here; not because of what you do, but simply because you exist.

Trusting this, you can lean into the belief that part of your Soul's Journey is knowing you bring unique gifts and contributions to the world, just by being. They show up in any number of ways, from the way you smile or, the energy you bring when you enter a room, to the more concrete, like your ability to make a delicious meal from whatever happens to be in the cupboard or doing a perfect pirouette on pointe. All of you matters, especially your happiness, so pursuing your unique gifts, following your heart's desires, and living authentically makes a difference to the planet.

You are and always have been on a journey of the Soul. Having cancer has just made it much more evident.

You are and always have been on a journey of the Soul, having cancer has just made it much more evident. For some reason, this was something your Soul wanted you to experience. Not out of punishment, but out of love, a love greater than you can imagine or have the capacity to fully experience. It's something you may never understand, but it's so much more freeing when you accept that whatever journey you are on, it's to help you on your path to living your most authentic life, as these stories of our clients show.

> *Daniel was burned-out from constantly being the "minister-on-call" for his demanding congregation. His cancer was a wake-up call. As the embers of "being of service" smoldered, he embraced his allies—of family and a love of learning—to recharge. This led him to a new way of providing service, offering one-on-one support.*

> *Sophia had been mad at her mother ever since she could remember. But when she learned to forgive herself in Allies, she also felt that forgiveness flowing out toward her mother who had done the best she could with six kids to raise. Now she calls her mother once a week, and they are getting to know each other without all the judgment and baggage.*

Lynn, already trapped in a toxic relationship, felt that cancer was one more thing she couldn't control. When, in The Pit, she learned to surrender to her emotions, out poured tears, screams, anger, sorrow, hopelessness, and fear. Years of pent-up feelings were released, clearing space for her to find the person she once knew herself to be: the one who said what she wanted, asked for what she needed and believed that it was all possible. By reclaiming herself, she was able to let go of the relationship that had brought her so much pain.

These changes all took place because our clients realized they mattered. That their own happiness was not only important but essential to healing mentally, emotionally, and spiritually. Owning the fact that you matter allows you to recognize and claim more of who you truly are and what you desire in your life.

It bears repeating that living in Transformation fosters the courage and commitment to live your heart's desire, from moment to moment. It takes the serendipitous moments you began to experience in Breakthrough and turns them into beliefs, habits, and actions that give you more of what you want each day. Breakthrough gave insight into the possibilities and gifts of your journey. Now Transformation implores you to make your dreams a reality, one step at a time.

So, look around you because in case you hadn't noticed, you've arrived at the new ground of your life. Not only is it safe to dream big, now in hearing the whispers of a new calling, you are compelled to answer. You are being called to embrace your new reality. And you're ready. Your beautiful soul is strong. Your wisdom runs deep. Your courage has been tested and proven unbreakable. Dear one, what we are telling you is: It is time to soar.

ADDITIONAL EXERCISES

Exercise: Looking Back at Innocence

Take a moment to review the questions you answered in the exercise in Innocence *Reviewing your Life Before Cancer*. If you didn't answer them then, you may want to take some time to reflect on them now. This is a means of tracking the changes you made throughout your cancer journey.

For your convenience, we've included the writing prompts again here:

- What was happening in your life? Describe a typical day.

- What did you dream about? What were your hopes for the future?

- What were you tolerating? This might take a few moments to connect to because the things that we "tolerate" become the norm like background noise. For example, I always sleep on my right side because my left shoulder hurts; my husband doesn't talk to me when he comes home from work, but it's okay because I know he's tired; my boss is disrespectful lots of the time, but I just ignore it.

- What did you dream about doing "someday" when everything—money, time, and situations—lined up?

After you've read through and reflected on your answers, spend a little time journaling about your discoveries. What's changed? Are your dreams the same, bigger? Are you tolerating less than before? Does your "someday" dream feel more real?

Exercise: Who Are You Now? A Daily Inquiry

Pick one of the questions/inquiries below. Allow it to linger in the forefront of your mind throughout the day. You can write down what you notice as you go along, or you can use the inquiry as inspiration for a longer journaling exercise. Pick whatever question appeals to you on any given day. Remain curious and engage your imagination.

- What have I learned and discovered on my cancer journey?

- How have I changed?

- Who am I now?

- How do I want and choose to live?

- What am I doing and who am I with when I am happiest?

- What is important (values) to me now?

- How am I living from my gifts, talents, and desires?

- If I could live my heart and soul's desire and didn't have to earn money, what would I be called to do?

- What do I want for my world? (Often found in what makes you angry or breaks your heart)

Exercise: Guided Imagery/Visualization: Embracing Your New Transformed Self and Your New Reality

Being and exploring your Transformed Self and new reality in a safe space allows you to get comfortable with expanding into who you are becoming—at your own pace. This guided visualization can be your "safe space" to do just that. You may want to read the following through a few times until you have it in your mind's eyes. That way, you can put this book aside and just go with the flow of the visualization.

Start by getting into a comfortable place either sitting or lying down and close your eyes. Take three deep breaths and extend your exhale with each breath. Inhale love in, and exhale love out.

Now imagine that you're at the top of a staircase and at the bottom is a door that will lead you to your happy and safe place. As you walk down the staircase, you are releasing the energy of your everyday world. At the bottom of the stairs, open the door and step into your safe place.

Take in your surroundings—what do you see? Smell? Hear? How does the air feel on your skin? Use your senses to connect with this safe and welcoming space.

In this safe space, find a comfortable place to sit and be. As you do, notice a light in the distance approaching you. As it gets closer, you notice that it's a person—a familiar person. And you recognize it is as you, the new transformed you, who is here for a conversation.

Welcome the new you and invite them to have a seat. They begin to share about who you were before your cancer journey; what you have endured and faced, and some of the discoveries along the way. You are both taking in and receiving your growth journey together.

Now, your Transformed Self tells you about whom you have become and are becoming. Where all the trials and tribulations led and where they might continue to lead. Listen and take in all that they want to share. Some come in words, others in pictures, some through sensations.

Take a long pause and allow these new reflections to sink in and mix with your current perception of yourself. Notice how you're feeling. Allow your emotions to arise in response to the embrace of your Transformed Self, and as you do, allow yourself to meld with them.

Allow yourself to rest in this safe space. And, when you're ready, thoughts of the door you opened to get here come to mind, and you are there.

As you open it, you find the stairs. Slowly climb the staircase counting from 1 to 5, and return to this present time and space, knowing you've become more of your Transformed Self. Take a deep breath. Open your eyes. You are back.

When you return to your present time, you might want to take 10 minutes to write down anything that you want to remember from this time with your Transformed Self. You can revisit this guided visualization/imagery whenever and as often as you'd like.

CHAPTER EIGHT
THE CONCLUSION

CONVENTIONAL WISDOM: Life is about getting to the finish line.

CANCER JOURNEY INSTITUTE WISDOM: Life is an adventure when you allow yourself to consciously grow and evolve. There is no such thing as a finish line.

"You are allowed to be both a masterpiece and
a work in progress simultaneously."
–SOPHIA BUSH

Shariann's Story: I Have Something Here!

Laptop nestled on my lap I sit to write my "Morning Pages," an attempt to capture the thoughts circling in my mind. They flow faster than my fingers can type today. The words organize themselves into a series of workshops and coaching programs to address the mental, emotional and spiritual needs of cancer patients, survivors and caregivers. Yup, I'm taking on the full lot. What I want most for my own cancer journey is unveiling itself on the page: roadmap, exercises, deep discussions, a safe and nurturing space.

"Oh, that feels good. I'm proud of what I created," I say to myself after I'm done writing. "I think I'll take it for a test run." As if divinely guided in that moment, the name of my friend at the University of California San Francisco's Cancer Center pops into my head. "I'll give Cindy a call to see if this would work for her audience."

Sitting at the large conference table in an annex to the Cancer Resource Center, Cindy introduces the two other women managers she brought to our meeting. "I liked what you said on the phone, Shariann, and thought that these key folks would be interested in hearing what you had to offer too."

I can barely hear my own thoughts through the drumming of my heartbeat. I begin to present my ideas for a series of workshops and personal coaching, sprinkling in my own personal cancer experience. I want to demonstrate that I understand the cancer individual's plight. I see nods of approval. Taking in a deep breath, I ask, "So, what do you think?"

"We like what you have to offer. To make it an official program, we'll have to pay you." I'm jolted for a moment. Did they say that they would have to pay me? "We also need to know how you plan to serve the volume of cancer patients that might want this." I ask for more time to figure out the logistics and promise them that I will get back to them in the coming weeks.

I walk out of the meeting in a trance, part elation and part shock. "Pay me! Large number of cancer patients? I have something here!" Another epiphany sparks…I can only handle twenty clients, max. I need more Cancer Coaches. I need to train some coaches. Who can I ask to help me? Again, a name pops into my head…Keri Lehmann!

It was a natural realization. Who was my favorite coach training instructor? Keri. Who was the one I chose to be my very first Life Coach and helped me through my hardest times of cancer? Keri. Who had the skills, tools, and talent to create something special with me? KERI! Over tea at our favorite Starbucks, I ask her if she would be interested in helping me train Cancer Journey Coaches and without missing a beat, she says, "YES!"

To seal the new partnership, we toast with our paper teacups, do a little "celebration" dance as we rise from our seats, link arms and joyously skip to our cars. The Cancer Journey Coaching movement begins.

We both still remember that feeling of skipping to the car, the exhilaration of imagining the program we would create for newly diagnosed cancer individuals and cancer survivors. What we couldn't know then, of course, was how many people's lives we would be privileged to touch. Or how many Cancer Journey Coaches we would train. Or how—and this really is the most important thing—The Cancer Journey Institute would begin to change the conversation around cancer.

Our efforts are paying off. We *are* shifting the conversation, from the notion of battling cancer as a deadly diagnosis to one of honoring it as an initiation into a profound soul journey. We stand in the conviction that it's not only possible but also likely that you will emerge from your cancer journey with a greater understanding of your true self.

We strongly believe that as long as this map is withheld from the world, countless individuals will continue to be traumatized by their cancer diagnoses. And many more will miss the opportunity to love and live their lives as individuals who know they truly matter.

Where We Are Today

Today our work is no longer on the fringes. What seemed like an impossible dream is starting to enter the mainstream. We have been featured in *The Wall Street Journal, Cure Today, Thrive Global* and *Authority Magazine*. Our work has been cited in books like *Braving Chemo* by Beverley A Zavaleta, MD and written about in *Stanford Medicine Magazine*. What that tells us is that we have sparked a new dialogue. This has always been our desire: to change the way you experience cancer. We believe the world is ready to embrace a new cancer paradigm.

And apparently, cancer isn't going away any time soon. Since we began this work, cancer diagnoses continue to increase at an astonishing rate. Not only that, but, as you may be aware, more people are also living with cancer. According to the National Cancer Institute, an estimated 19.3 million new cases of cancer were diagnosed, globally, in 2020.[1] A large percentage of those diagnosed will continue to live with cancer for years after diagnosis. Many will move on to NED (No Evidence of Disease.) Cancer is part of the human condition.

We are at the forefront of the "journey mindset," the mindset that holds cancer as a wake-up call. It is a call to greater wholeness, healing, and personal growth. Above all, it is an *opportunity* to step into the person you were destined to become. Today, we are dreaming another dream, that this book you hold is the guidebook and the map that allows you to make this journey.

1. Source: GLOBOCAN 2020 – https://acsjournals.onlinelibrary.wiley.com/doi/full/10.3322/caac.21660).

You Are Now Part of The Movement

This book began as a hope and a dream. The biggest part of that dream is that the book would get into your hands so that you could stand on our shoulders and those of others who have traveled this path before you. And not only did you open it, but you also tried it on. And in the process, you took a journey of transformation.

We wanted to give you the experience of being changed by our love, but more importantly, by your own.

You are now part of The Cancer Journey movement. In the Introduction, we invited you to imagine all of us, from all across the world, linking arms with each other, reminding you that you are part of something bigger. And you *are* part of something bigger. We also wanted you to know that you can love your way through this. And you said, yes. Now you are part of that dream, and our global dream team.

Thank you for being courageous enough to embrace this new cancer paradigm. It takes courage to hold up the mirror that this book offers. It takes commitment to embark on the deep inner quest to look at your patterns, challenges, and fears. And it takes determination to realize the breadth and depth of your power and to let that knowledge change your life.

Each of us has the capacity to choose how we will take this journey. And you chose to make it a deeply personal, profoundly powerful process of discovery. By making that choice, you have paved the way for someone else to follow in your footsteps. You have helped to alleviate unnecessary pain and suffering, while discovering your most authentic self.

Our hope is to perpetuate the concept of a journey mindset, and that it becomes the norm to seek *whole healing* by getting support for the emotional, spiritual, and mental aspects of the journey, just as much as for the physical. Because it's all interconnected.

What we've also discovered is that as we embrace our wholeness as human beings, we also want to be part of the healing process for others.

This is why we created The Cancer Journey Institute to train people to walk with those on a cancer journey, using the tools and techniques you've experienced in this book—and so much more.

This Book Is a Guide for Living

We hope this book has become your close companion: a source of comfort so that the pages are well worn, dog-eared and highlighted. We believe the maps, tools, and concepts within it can support you as you continue your life journey. Use them for yourself or share them with others.

We want you to know, you can turn to the wisdom in these pages as challenges arise during the course of your life. Because as inevitably happens, you will be called to something more. Now you have a guide. You can use this book whenever you choose to answer a new call to set out on a different road than the one you're currently on. So, as you close these pages, keep The Call of Cancer: *a Loving Pathway to Wholeness, Healing, and Personal Growth* close at hand. You never know when you might need its comfort and wisdom.

As we stated at the beginning of this book, our promise to you is "*to be with you every step of the way.*" We hope you have felt that as you traveled the roadmap within this book.

In our Cancer Journey Coach Certification Program, our coaches-in-training, all of who have had cancer experiences of their own, are put through the paces of our body of work. At the end of their training, we ask them to make promises to themselves. We share some of them with you here, by way of completion. We hope to inspire you to craft your own.

> "*I promise to remember how much this work feeds healthy growth, restoration, discovery, play, and to plug into that, like digging my toes into a fresh garden.*" ~**Paige**

"I promise to give myself permission to lean into myself, into what I bring to the world, and to trust myself." **~Shelyna**

"I promise to continue to reflect on my transformation and my Soul's Journey." **~Denise**

"I promise to remember that everything I need to heal is within me." **~Tom**

"I promise to remain committed to who I am and what I want to do with my life." **~Amy**

"I promise to listen to my heart, my body, and my soul. **~Sally**

"I promise to bring all of myself as I continue to walk this path of growth and self-exploration, with love as the motivator. And so it is." **~Maggie**

"I promise to listen—to myself first, especially," **~Mark**

"I promise to have confidence in myself and to trust the Universe because I know that this is the right path." **~Susanna**

"I promise to continue to hold space for myself and others." **~Martina**

"I promise to honor myself by connecting and allowing my emotions to lead me on my Soul's Journey." **~Catherine**

We will close with the message we give to all our beloved clients, friends, and allies. Remember, ***"You are more powerful—and loved—than you realize."***

NOTES

For additional tools and resources (like audios of the guided visualizations) to help you implement the concepts from this book, please visit us at www.thecancerjourney.com. We invite you to join our community of Cancer Individuals and Cancer Journey Coaches.

www.thecancerjourney.com

REFERENCES

Introduction

The Cancer Journey Roadmap
is loosely based on Joseph Campbell's Hero's Journey, from The Hero with a Thousand Faces, Pantheon Books, 1949

The Call

"Do the best you can until you know better. When you know better, do better."
Maya Angelou, November 16, 2015

Victim-Warrior
adapted from Great Story Coaching, Lucid Living 2005, www.lucidliving.net

"Creating healthy boundaries...including the one you have with yourself,"
from Boundary Boss: the essential guide to talk true, be seen and (finally) live free by Terri Cole. Sounds True Publishing, Boulder, CO, 2021

Initiation

"...your mind is designed to perceive and anticipate threats..." from Team Up! Applying Lessons from Neuroscience to Improve Collaboration, Innovation and Results, Lori Shook & Frode Svensen, August 24, 2014

The Pit

The Emotions Map
from The Tiers of Emotion, Copyright 2005, Concept: Synergy, Inc.
Concept: Synergy, P.O. Box 1789, Sonoma, CA 95476

*"The deeper that **sorrow** carves into your being, the more joy you can contain."* from Kahlil Gibran's The Prophet, 1923

"Toxic Positivity: the belief that no matter how dire or difficult a situation is, people should be positive." from Toxic Positivity: Don't Always Look on the Bright Side. truly process your emotions instead, Konstantin Lukin, Ph.D.

Wounded Ego
adapted from A New Earth: Awakening to Your Life's Purpose by Eckhart Tolle Plume Publishing, 2006; Copyright Eckart Tolle, 2005

Best Memory Exercise
from Co-Active Training Institute's Fulfillment Workshop; 899 Northgate Drive, Suite 304, San Rafael, CA 94903

Wheel of Life
from CoActive Coaching: New Skills for Coaching People toward Success in Work and Life, Davies-Black publishing, Mountain View, CA, Copyright 2007

Ranking and Rating Values
from CoActive Coaching: New Skills for Coaching People toward Success in Work and Life, Davies-Black publishing, Mountain View, CA, Copyright 2007

Beginning Chapter Quotes

Innocence: "Innocence tinctures all things with the brightest hues."—Edward Counsel, "Maxims: Political, Philosophical and Moral"

The Call: "Life is what happens while you're busy making other plans."—John Lennon, January,1957

Initiation: "The thing you fear most has no power. Your fear of it is what has the power. Facing the truth really will set you free."—Oprah Winfrey

The Pit: "Vulnerability sounds like truth and feels like courage. These aren't always comfortable, but they are never weakness."—Brene Brown, The Power of Vulnerability, Sounds True, Inc. November 15, 2012

Allies: Allies are the things that nourish and awaken our true selves. They lift us and assure us that we are not alone."—Shariann Tom, 2020

Breakthrough: "A Breakthrough is a moment in time when the impossible becomes possible."—Tony Robbins

Transformation: Transformation is a process, and as life happens there are tons of ups and downs. It's a journey of discovery."—Rick Warren

ACKNOWLEDGMENTS

This book would not have been possible without the love, support, and guidance of the following people. We want to thank those mentioned here, and the countless others who were there for us during our writing adventures and who supported us on our cancer journeys. You have had immeasurable impact on our lives, our work, and this book.

Thank you to our beloved clients who have courageously shared their journeys with us. To Mary Reynolds Thompson, who championed us, propped us up and kept us focused monthly, weekly and daily. To our outstanding publishing team, Martha Bullen, Christy Day, Maggie McLaughlin, and Gail Snyder, who held our hands, all the way through the book publishing process, and to our infinitely patient graphics and technical wizard, Kevin Hoelscher. To Mary Coughlin, who helped us bring the concepts and tools to life, and to Liana Smith, who partnered with us throughout the process of writing this book. To our Global Tribe of Cancer Journey Coaches, whose undying faith and passion in the roadmap and all it contains kept us going.

Finally, and perhaps most importantly, we'd like to acknowledge our dear husbands, Gerry Tom and Jay Lehmann, along with our caring and compassionate family (Dylan, Ryan, Alicia, and the Wong and Felsher clan) who gave us tremendous support, had seemingly tireless patience and words of encouragement, not only for the book, but over the last decade of co-creating The Cancer Journey Institute. We wouldn't be here today if it weren't for you!

ABOUT SHARIANN TOM

SHARIANN TOM is the co-founder and Chief Executive Officer of The Cancer Journey Institute. Her life was transformed after she experienced two turning points: surviving four bouts of Hodgkin's Lymphoma and one bout of a Gastric Intestinal Stromal Tumor (GIST) and making life coaching her profession.

The profound contrast between facing cancer without a coach and embarking on a cancer journey with a coach by her side inspired Shariann to start a movement dedicated to cancer patients, caregivers, and survivors. She believes that everyone facing cancer would benefit from having a Cancer Journey Coach (CJC) to help them heal emotionally and spiritually and find their true power.

Shariann has nearly 25 years of coaching and coach training experience combined with 16 years in corporate America, which gives her the expertise needed to lead and operate an innovative company and to support the growing number of CJCs worldwide.

Shariann lives with her husband, Gerry, in the San Francisco Bay Area where she can be near her family, her number one value, which includes her children and fur babies.

ABOUT KERI LEHMANN

 KERI LEHMANN is the co-founder and Chief Spiritual Officer (CSO) for The Cancer Journey Institute. Her journey with breast cancer in 2019 challenged her to put self-love first, no matter what.

A pioneer in the coaching industry, Keri has nearly three decades of experience as a coach and as a facilitator of coach training for The Co-Active Training Institute (CTI). She earned an M.A. in Human Resource Development from The George Washington University in Washington, D.C. and a Master Certified Coach designation from The International Coaching Federation.

Keri has also studied metaphysics. She believes that love is the greatest healing elixir and that when someone learns to love themselves, transformative healing is possible.

Keri lives with her husband, Jay, in Pacifica, a coastal town in the San Francisco Bay area, where she enjoys daily beach walks with their handsome mixed-breed dog, Bosco.

Learn more about both authors and this book at
www.TheCancerJourney.com.

Made in the USA
Middletown, DE
02 April 2023

28133987R00116